A Union List of Publications

in

Opaque Microforms

1961 Supplement

compiled by

Eva Maude Tilton

The Scarecrow Press, Inc.

New York   1961

Foreword

This supplement, like the original, is a compilation of opaque microprint reproductions and follows the pattern set up there. It, however, contains listings from European, as well as American publishers. It is not a bibliography in the ordinary sense of the word since accurate bibliographic information is not always available and it has been felt better to use the information as supplied by the publisher. Effort has been made to reproduce the information accurately; errors of this kind are strictly the fault of the compiler.

All information it has been possible to obtain from various sources has been included. The compiler regrets any omissions and will be pleased to receive notice of material omitted which should be included. One item in this category is the Microcard Catalogue of the Kaufman Collection, edited by R. Gergely, a publication of the Oriental Library of the Hungarian Academy of Sciences, which came to the compiler's attention too late to include in proper order.

With a very few exceptions, the entries are those given by the publisher which results in a list oriented to key word rather than to rigid catalog entry. Most of the entries, however, are by author. Cross references among the main entries have been used both to direct attention to pseudonyms and to material entered under simplified headings.

The index aims to bring out the names of joint authors, editors, and so forth as well as broad subject fields. The index itself has presented a problem with whose solution the compiler is by no means entirely satisfied. Since the compilation itself is already an index, a problem has been posed as to how exhaustive its index should be. The com-- piler is quite aware the index is rudimentary, but indexing an index has appeared somewhat futile. Comment or suggestions will be appreciated.

iii

Publishers Listed and Sumbols Used

Several of the publishers use a code number with
various individual titles to indicate either subject field or
a group which is available at a special rate. A code
number has been provided to indicate these groupings.

The entries, with the exception noted below, are all
of material on standard Microcards. Some of these--not
indicated--are now double faced.

The arrangement here has been changed from that
originally used to bring the publisher symbols into alpha-
betic order rather than an order based on the key word
of the publisher's name.

Publisher Symbol		Code Symbols

AB American Bar Foundation
1155 East 60th Street
Chicago, Illinois

ACS American Chemical Society
Special Issues Sales Department
1155 Sixteenth Street, N.W.
Washington 6, D.C.

AI American Institute of Biological Sciences
2000 P Street, N.W.
Washington 6, D.C.

AmG American Geographical Society
Broadway at 156th Street
New York 32, New York

ASTIA Armed Services Technical Information Agency
Air Research and Development Command
United States Air Force
Arlington Hall Station
Arlington 12, Virginia

B   Matthew Bender & Company, Inc.
443 Fourth Avenue
New York 16, New York

C   J.S. Canner & Company, Inc.
46 Millmont Street
Boston 19, Massachusetts
Publications may also be ordered from
their affiliate organization: Microcan, Inc.

F   Microcard Foundation
901 Twenty-sixth Street, N.W.
Washington 7, D.C.

GML   Godfrey Memorial Library
Middletown, Connecticut
Genealogical material previously listed
with the symbol, GI (American Genealogical
Index), is now included here

KU   University of Kentucky Press
Lexington, Kentucky

LC   Library of Congress
Robert H. Land, Secretary
Committee on Bibliography & Publications
Washington 25, D.C.

LoC   Lost Cause Press
Charles & Nancy Farnsley
235 South Galt Avenue
Louisville 6, Kentucky
British Culture on Microcards:
        Group 3   BC-3
        Group 4   BC-4
History of Science: HS-1
Kentucky Culture Series:
        Group 8   KC-8
        Group 9   KC-9

Publisher Symbol		Code Symbols
	Group 10	KC-10
	Group 11	KC-11
	Group 12	KC-12
	Group 13	KC-13
	Group 14	KC-14
	Mike Fink Miscellany:	MFM
	Nineteenth Century American Literature:	
	The Ohio Valley; Series A, Group 5	OV-A5
	The South; Series B, Group 3	S-B3
	The South; Series B, Group 4	S-B4
	The Plains and the Rockies:	
	Group 1	P&R-1
	Group 2	P&R-2
	Travels in the Old South	
	Group 1	TOS-1
	Group 2	TOS-2
	Group 3	TOS-3
	Group 4	TOS-4

MMe   Micro Methods, Ltd.
East Ardsley, Wakefield
Yorks, England

MK   Mikrokopie-Verlag, Dr. J. Goebel
Mainz und Den Haag
52, Conradkade, The Hague
The Netherlands
Every title includes an order number;
indicates a 9 x 12 cm. positive film,
which costs Dfl. 1, 50. If required, a
print on "microprint-carton" is delivered
at the same price.

MMP   E.P. Danger
Microprint Publications, Ltd.
1-2 Botolph Alley, Eastcheap
London, E.C. 3, England
      or
U.S. representative:
Oceana Publications, Inc.
80 Fourth Avenue
New York 3, New York
   Pre-1865 Law Reports [England
   & Wales]   LR-E&W

Publisher Symbol		Code Symbols
MXT	Microtext Publishing Corporation 112 Liberty Street New York 6, New York	
O	University of Oregon Health & Physical Education Microcards Eugene, Oregon	
	Health education	HE-(no.)
	Physical education	PE-(no.)
	Physiology of exercise	PH-(no.)
	Psychology	PSY-(no.)
	Recreation & Camping	RC-(no.)
RDX**	Readex Microprint Corporation 100 Fifth Avenue New York 11, New York	
SM	Peter Smith 20 Railroad Avenue Gloucester, Massachusetts	
UR	University of Rochester Press Rush Rhees Library River Campus Station Rochester 20, New York	
	ACRL Microcard Series:	ACRL-(no.)

**6 x 9 double faced, lithographed cards

Acknowledgements

At this time, I wish to make grateful acknowledgement of the encouragement and co-operation which made the original book and this supplement possible: first of all, to the publishers whose co-operation and information have been basic; second, but equally important, to Mr. John B. Nicholson, Jr., Librarian of Kent State University, Kent, Ohio, and head of the Library Science Department there, whose idea for a thesis it originally was; to Mrs. Margaret K. Toth, editor of the University of Rochester Press who first suggested the material should be published; to my niece and nephew, Constance and Timothy Tilton, and to Marlene Lattimer, all of whom gave me invaluable aid on the tiresome task of copyreading; and last, but by no means least, all the people, too numerous to mention individually, much as they deserve it, who have listened so patiently to my frettings over the problems involved and without whose encouragement the task never would have been finished.

Eve Tilton
Bozeman, Montana

Abbildung eines sonderbahren Lufft-Schiffes. Oder, Kunzt
zu fliegen. Wien, 1709, Sign.: 30:S9/1983 Nr. 203. MK 1

Abdy, Edward Strutt (OV-A5)--Journal of a residence and
tour in the United States of North America, from April,
1833 toOctober, 1834. London, J. Murray, 1835. 3v.
vl, 6.94; v2, 4.95; v3, 4.95 LoC   2

Abercromby, Patrick (BC-4)--The martial achievements of
the Scots nation. 1711-15. 2v. 4.95 each LoC   3

Abraham Africanus I (AP-1)--His secret life, as revealed
under the mesmeric influence. Mysteries of the White
House. New York, J.F. Feeks, 1864. 57p. 2.45 LoC 4

Adair, James (TOS-1)--The history of the American Indians;
particularly those nations adjoining to the Mississippi,
East and West Florida, Georgia, South and North
Carolina, and Virginia; ... Also an appendix. London,
printed for E. & C. Dilly, 1755. 5.95 LoC   5

Adam, Marylou Merkel (PSY-104)--Secular trends in
women's body proportions. 1959. Thesis (M.S.)
Pennsylvania State Univ. 52p. 1.15 O   6

Adams--The novels of Ramon J. Sender. 1.40 KU   7

Adams, C.F.--Chapters of Erie and other Essays. 3.25 SM8

Adams, C.F.--Familiar letters of John Adams and his wife,
Abigail Adams, during the Revolution. 3.00 SM   9

Adams, J.Q.--Memoirs, ed. by Charles Francis Adams.
12v. 35.00 SM   10

Adams, Shirley Lou (HE-46)--Health misconceptions among
students enrolled in freshman health classes at the
University of Oregon. 1959. Thesis (M.S.), Univ.
of Oregon. 55p. 1.15 O   11

Adams, W.E. (AP-1)--The slaveholders' war: an argument
for the north and the Negro. Manchester, Union &
Emancipation Soc., 1863. 24p. 2.45 LoC   12

Adams, W.F.--Ireland and Irish emigration to the New
World from 1815 to the Famine. 3.50 SM   13

Agardh, Jacob Georg--Analecta algologica. Observationes de speciebus algarum minus cognitis earumque dispositione. Lund, 1892-1899 (Includes Continuatios I-V). 6.75 F   14

Agardh, Karl Adolph--Species algarum rite cognitae, cum synonymis differentiis specificis et descriptionibus succinctis. Gryphiswaldiae, 1823-28. 2v. 4.00 F   15

Agardh, Karl Adolph--Synopsis algarum scandinaviae, adjecta dispositione universali algarum. Lundae, 1817. 1.00 F   16

Agardh, Karl Adolph--Systema algarum. Lundae, 1824. 1.75 F   17

Agricola, Martin--Musica choralis deudsch. Wittemberg, 1533. 1.00 UR   18

Aikin, J. (BC-4)--An essay on the plan and character of Thompson's Seasons. 1778. 4.95 LoC   19

Aimard, Gustave (P&R-2)--The Trail Hunter; a tale of the Far West. 5.95 LoC   20

Alden, Edgar H.--The role of the motive in musical structure. 1956. Thesis (Ph.D.), Univ. of North Carolina. 2.25 UR   21

Alexander, James Waddel (S-B4)--Forty years' familiar letters ... constituting, with notes, a memoir of his life. Ed. by the surviving correspondent, John Hall. New York, C. Scribner; (etc.), 1860. 2v. 3.95 each LoC   22

Alexis (BC-4); or The young adventurer. A novel. 1746. 4.95 LoC   23

Allemagne, d' (TOS-1)--Nouvelles du Scioto, ... Paris, Chez Lenoir & Leboucher, 1790. 5.95 LoC   24

Allen, Miss A.J. (P&R-1)--Ten years in Oregon. Travels and adventures of Dr. E. White and lady, west of the Rocky Mountains; ... 5.95 LoC   25

Allen, George--General history of the Allen family
from 1568 to 1882. By Wm. Allen. Farmington, Me.,
1882. 31p. .80 GML   26

Allen, George, Sup.--Supplement to the Allen family.
By Wm. Allen. Salem, Mass., 1891. 24p. .80 GML 27

Allen, Walt.--Walter Allen of Newbury, Mass., 1640
and some of his descendants. By Allen H. Bent.
Boston, 1896. 66p. 1.40 GML   28

Allgemeine Deutsche Biographie. proposed, 275.00 F   29

Allgemeine Musikalische Zeitung. Vols. 1-10 (1798/99-
1807/08). 65.00 Vols. 11-40 (1809-1848) to be
issued in 10 vol. units, all to be available by June of
1962.   UR   30

Alsop, George (TOS-1)--A character of the province of
Mary-land, wherein is described in four distinct parts,
(viz.) I. The scituation, and plenty of the province.
II. The laws, customs, and natural demeanor of the
inhabitant. III. The worst and best usage of a Maryland servant, ... IV. The traffique and vendable
commodities ... Also a small treatise on the wilde
and naked Indians (or Susquehanokes) ... Together
with a collection of historical letters. London, Printed
by T.J. for P. Dring, 1666. 5.95 LoC   31

Alter und verbesserter Schreib-Kalender, auf das G.G.
Gnadenreiche Christ-Jahp MDCCLV (TOS-1). ...
St. Gallen, Hans Jacob Hochreuetiner, 1754. 5.95
LoC   32

Altsheler, Joseph Alexander (S-B4)--A herald of the
West; an American story of 1811-1815. New York,
D. Appleton & Co., 1898. 359p. 3.95 LoC   33

--------(S-B4)--A soldier of Manhattan and his adventures at Ticonderoga and Quebec. New York,
D. Appleton & Co., 1897. vi, 316p. 3.95 LoC   34

--------(S-B4)--The sun of Saratoga, a romance of
Burgovne's surrender. New York, D. Appleton & Co.,
1897. 313p. 3.95 LoC   35

Amar, Jules (PE-403)--The human motor; or, the scientific foundations of labour and industry. Published by G. Routledge, London; E.P. Dutton, New York, 1920. 470p. 2.85 O   36

An American, pseud. (AP-1)--Letter on American slavery. Addressed to the editor of the "Witness," 8th July 1846. Edinburgh, printed by Miller & Fairly, 1846. 12p. 2.45 LoC   37

American Anthropologist. New series. Vols. 1-50 (1899-1948). 330.00 C   38

American Association of Petroleum Geologists. Bulletin. Vols. 11-30 (1927-1946). 242.50 C   39

American Civil War (AP-1)--Correspondence with Mr. H.C. Carey, of Philadelphia, Aug.-Sept., 1861. N.p., 1861. 23p. 2.45 LoC   40

American Enterprise (P&R-2)--"In the issue of May 13, 1813, the Missouri Gazette of St. Louis published a short account of the return trip of Robert Stuart, Ramsay Crooks, and Robert McClellan from Astoria to St. Louis. ..." 5.95 LoC   41

American Fisheries Society. Transactions. Vols. 1-75 (1872-1945). 215.00 C   42

The American gazeteer (TOS-2). Containing a distinct account of all parts of the New World; ... London, printed for A. Millar, & J.&R. Tonson, 1762. 3v. 5.95 each LoC   43

American Journal of Psychiatry. Vols. 108-113 (1951-57). 50.00 UR   44

American Journal of Science. Vols. 248-49 (1950-51). 14.00 C   45

American Journal of Sociology. Vols. 1-24 (1895-1919). 143.50; in prep, vols. 25-28. C   46

American Journal of the Medical Sciences. Vol. 237- (1959-). 5.00 per vol.; proposed: New Series; vols. 1-236 (1841-1958), 1300.00 F   47

American Journal of Veterinary Research. Vols. 1-17
(1940-1956). 67.50   C   48

American Pamphlets--See Nineteenth Century American
Pamphlets.

American Physical Education Review:
(PE-404).   Vol. 21 (1916)   561p.   3.65
(PE-405).   Vol. 22 (1917)   572p.   3.65
(PE-406).   Vol. 23 (1918)   565p.   3.45
(PE-407).   Vol. 24 (1919)   527p.   3.65
(PE-408).   Vol. 25 (1920)   414p.   3.20
(PE-427).   Vol. 26 (1921)   450p.   3.20
(PE-428).   Vol. 27 (1922)   504p.   3.20
(PE-429).   Vol. 28 (1923)   496p.   3.45
(PE-430).   Vol. 29 (1924)   624p.   3.85   O   49

American plays---See Drama of the 19th Century.

American Society for Horticultural Science. Proceedings.
Vols. 1-27 (1903-1930).   82.00   C   50

American State Papers. Serial nos. 01-038. June 11,
1789-March 3, 1823. 38v. 125.00   RDX   51

Amerika (TOS-2), in alle zyne byzonderheden beschouwd,
ter verkryging einer naauwkeurige kennis van dat thans
zo veel gerucht maakend waerelddeel. .... Amsterdam,
Pieter Meiger, 1780-82. 4v. 5.95 each LoC   52

Ames, Joseph (BC-4)--Typographical Antiquities. 1749.
4.95 LoC   53

Amhurst, Nicholas (BC-4)--Terrae Filius, or the secret
history of the University of Oxford. 1726. 4.95 LoC   54

Amory, Thomas (BC-4)--Life of John Buncle, Esq.
1756-66. 2v. 4.95 each LoC   55

--------(BC-4)--Memoirs containing the lives of several
ladies of Great Britain. 1755. 4.95 LoC   56

Anderson, Charles (OV-A5)--An address on Anglo-Saxon
destiny. Cincinnati, printed by J.D. Thorpe, 1850.
48p. 2.52 LoC   57

--------(KC-9)--A funeral oration on the character, life, and public services of Henry Clay. Cincinnati, Ben Franklin Office Print, 1852. 38p. 2.50 LoC   58

--------(OV-A5)--An oration on the real nature and value or the American Revolution. Cincinnati, C.F. Bradley & Co., Printers, 1855. 31p. 2.50 LoC   59

Anderson, James (BC-4)--Selectus diplomatum et numis-matem Scotiae thesaurus. 1739. 4.95 LoC   60

Anderson, James [1739-1808] (BC-4)--An account of the present state of the Hebrides and western coasts of Scotland. 1785. 4.95 LoC   61

--------(BC-4)--Essays relating to agriculture and rural affairs. 1775. 4.95 LoC   62

--------(BC-4)--The interest of Great Britain with regard to her American colonies considered. 1782. 4.95 LoC 63

Anderson, Robert (BC-4)--The life of Samuel Johnson. 1795. 4.95 LoC   64

Andros Tracts. Publications of the Prince Society. 3v. 10.00 SM   65

Angleria, Camillo--La regola del contraponto, e della mvsical compositione. Milano, 1622. 1.50 UR   66

Annet, Peter (BC-4)--A collection of the tracts of a certain free enquirer. 1739-45. 4.95 LoC   67

--------(BC-4)--The resurrection of Jesus considered. 3d ed. 1744. 4.95 LoC   68

Annual reports of all corporations, listed on the New York Stock Exchange, for the year: 1958   261.40
                                          1959   265.25
                                          sold on an annual subs.
basis - per card, 24 cents
listed on the American Stock Exchange, for the year:
1958   160.45
1959   161.26
sold on an annual subs. basis - per card 23 cents GML 69

Annual Review of Microbiology. Vols. 1-4 (1947-1950).
Per vol., 3.00   C   70

ACRL Microcard Series, 1-99 (ACRL-100). Abstracts
of titles included in the series. 1.00 UR   71

Arber, E., ed.--The first three English books on America,
1511-1555 A.D. 5.00 SM   72

Arbuthnot, Archibald, pseud. (BC-4)--The life adventures,
and many and great vicissitudes of Simon Lord Loval.
1746. 4.95   LoC   73

--------(BC-4)--Memoirs of the remarkable life and sur-
prising adventures of Miss Jenny Cameron. 1746.
4.95 LoC   74

Arbuthnot, John (BC-4)--Miscellaneous works. 1751.
2v. 4.95 each LoC   75

Arce, William Benjamin (PE-426)--Planning boys'
gymnasium facilities for secondary schools. 1956.
Thesis (Ed.D.), Stanford Univ. 364p. 2.65 O   76

Archdale, John (TOS-4)--A new description of that fertile
and pleasant province of Carolina; ... London, printed
for J. Wyat, 1707. 5.95 LoC   77

Armed Services Technical Information Agency. "Classified
and unclassified scientific and technical reports ...
to provide ... scientific and technical information of
value to the defense research and development community.
Does not serve the general public, which is served ...
by the Office of Technical Services of the U.S. Dept.
of Commerce." ASTIA   78

Armstrong, John (BC-4)--The art of preserving health.
1744. v.17 v.37 Med. (Hist.) 4.95 LoC   79

--------(BC-4)--Benevolence. An episode. 1751.
4.95 LoC   80

--------(BC-4)--A Day. An epistle of John Wilkes. 1761.
4.95 LoC   81

Ashe, Thomas [supposed author] (TOS-4)--Carolina;
or A description of the present state of that country
and the natural excellencies thereof, ... London,
printed for W. C. ... 1682. 5.95 LoC   95

--------(OV-A5)--Memoirs and confessions. London,
H. Colburn, 1815. 3v. v1, 5.84; v2, 3.85; v3,
3.85   LoC   96

--------(OV-A5)--Memoirs of Mammoth, and various other
extraordinary and stupendous bones, of incognita, or
nondescript animals, found in the vicinity of the Ohio,
Wabash, Illinois, Mississippi, Missouri, Osage, and
Red rivers, etc. Liverpool, Printed by G.F. Harris,
1806. 60p. 2.65   LoC   97

--------(TOS-1)--Travels in America, performed in
1806, ... London, Richard Phillips, 1808. 3v.
5.95 each LoC   98

--------(MFM, also OV-A4)--Travels in America, performed in 1806. 1808. 6.62 LoC   99

Association de la Propagation de la Foi (P&R-2). Notice
sur les Missions du Diocese de Quebec, ... Quebec,
de l'Imprimerie de Frechette & Cie. Imprimeurs et
libraires, No. 8, Rue La-Montagne. Avec approbation
des Superieurs. (1839-1874). 21v. 5.95 each
                                LoC   100

Aston, Anthony (TOS-1)--The fool's opera; or, The taste
of the age. Written by Mat Medley (pseud.) And
performed by his company in Oxford. To which is
prefix'd, A sketch of the author's life, written by himself. London, T. Payne (etc.), 1731?   5.95   LoC   101

Attmore, William (TOS-4)--Journal of a tour to North
Carolina ... 1787. [Ed. by L.T. Rodman]   Chapel
Hill, The University, 1922. 5.95 LoC   102

Atwater, Caleb (OV-A5)--The general character, present
and future prospects of the people of Ohio. An address
... Dec. 1826. Columbus, Printed by P.H. Olmsted
& Co., 1827. 21p. 2.50 LoC   103

Aubrey, John (BC-3)--Miscellanies upon various subjects.
4th ed. London, J.R. Smith, 1857. 227p. 4.49 LoC 104

Audubon, John James (TOS-2)--Journal ... made during
his trip to New Orleans in 1820-21. Ed. by H. Corning.
Foreword by R. Deane. Boston, Club of Odd Volumes,
1929. 5.95 LoC 105

Austin (LR-E&W)--County Court. 1v. (1867-69). MMP 106

Austin Dict.--Genealogical dictionary of R.I.: three
generations of settlers who came before 1690. By
John Osborne. Albany, N.Y., 1887. 450p. 14.00
GML 107

Avicenna, 980?-1037 (HS-1)--Libri in re medica omnes
qui hactenus ad nos peruenere. Venetiis, Apud V.
Valgrisium, 1564. 2v. 8.93 LoC 108

Ayliffe, J. (BC-4)--The ancient and present state of
the University of Oxford. 1714. 2v. 4.95 each LoC 109

--------(BC-4)--The case of Dr. Ayliffe at Oxford.
1716. 4.95 LoC 110

Ayres & Givens, firm, Louisville, Ky. (KC-13)--Eastern
Kentucky, a field for profitable investment.
Louisville, Courier-Journal Co., 1889. 24p. 2.50
LoC 111

B

B., T. (BC-4)--A criticism by T.B. on the New Sophonisba,
a tragedy. 1730. 4.95 LoC 112

B. de las Casas--Regionum indicarum per hispanos.
Heidelberg, 1664. Nr.154-156 (Bedeutendes, Vielums-
trittenes Werk mit erschütternden Abbildungen der
Greueltaten). MK 113

Back, George (P&R-2)--Narrative of the Arctic land
expedition to the mouth of the Great Fish River, and
along the shores of the Arctic Ocean, in the years
1833-35. 5.95 LoC 114

Bacon, Mrs. Lydia B. (Stetson) (TOS-3)--Journal ...
[1811-1812. Ms. copy; New York Hist. Soc. Library]
5.95 LoC   115

Badin, Stephen Theodore (TOS-1)--Origine et progres
de la mission du Kentucky, ... Paris, Adrien Le
Clere, 1821. 5.95 LoC   116

Bage, Robert (BC-4)--Barham Downs. 1784. 2v.
4.95 each LoC   117

--------(BC-4)--The fairsyrian. 1787. 4.95 LoC   118

--------(BC-4)--Hermsprong; or, Man as he is not.
1796. 2v. 4.95 each LoC   119

--------(BC-4)--James Wallace. 1788. 4.95 LoC   120

--------(BC-4)--Man as he is. 1792. 4.95 LoC   121

--------(BC-4)--Mount Henneth. 1781. 2v. 4.95 each
LoC   122

Bagg, Lyman Hotchkiss, 1846 (KC-14)--Ten thousand
miles on a bicycle. By Karl Kron (pseud.). New York,
Karl Kron, 1887. 799p. 3.95   LoC   123

Bailey, G. (KC-10)--The great caverns of Kentucky:
Diamond cave, Mammoth cave, Hundred dome cave.
Chicago, Church & Goodman (1863). 63p. 2.50 LoC 124

Baily, Francis (TOS-3)--Journal of a tour in unsettled
parts of North America, in 1796 & 1797. ... London,
Baily Brothers, 1856. 5.95 LoC   125

Baird, Henry Carey, 1825 (AP-1)--George Washington
and Gen. Jackson, on Negro soldiers. Philadelphia,
H.C. Baird, 1863. 8p. 2.45 LoC   126

Baird, Robert (OV-A5; also listed as part of MFM
series with a date of 1834)--View of the Valley of
the Mississippi; or, The emigrant's and traveller's
guide to the West. Philadelphia, H.S. Tanner, 1832.
341p. 5.74 LoC   127

11

Barbe, Waitman (S-B4)--Ashes and incense, poems.
Philadelphia, J.B. Lippincott Co. ... 158p.
3.95 LoC   140

--------(S-B3)--In the Virginias, stories and sketches.
Illus. by John Rettig. Akron, O., The Werner Co.,
1896. ... 184p. 3.25 LoC   141

Barber, Mary (BC-4)--Poems on several occasions.
1734. 4.95 LoC   142

Barclay, James (BC-4)--An examination of Mr. Kenrick's
review (of Dr. Johnson's new ed. of Shakespeare).
1766. 4.95 LoC   143

Barclay, Robert (BC-4)--A modest and serious address
to the well meaning follower of Ant. Bourignon.
1708. 4.95 LoC   144

Barker Gen.--The Barker genealogy. By James C.
Parshall. Middletown, N.Y., 1897. 36p. .80 GML145

Barron & Arnold (LR-E&W)--Election. 1v. (1842);
1v. (1843-46). MMP   146

Barry, Joseph, 1828? (AP-1)--The annals of Harper's
Ferry, from the establishment of the national armory
in 1794 to the present time, 1869. ... by Josephus,
Jr. (pseud.). Hagerstown, Md., Dechert & Co.,
printers, 1869. 64p. 2.45 LoC   167

Barry, Thomas (TOS-1)--Narrative of ... captivity ...
among the Monsipi Indians, ... during the years
1797-99: ... Written by himself. Manchester,
T. Thomas & J. Sadler [1800] 5.95 LoC   168

Bartlett, John Russell (P&R-2)--Personal narrative of
explorations and incidents in Texas, New Mexico,
California, Sonora and Chihuahua, connected with
the United States and Mexican Boundary Commission,
during the years 1850-53. 2v. 5.95 each LoC   169

Bartholoman's Yorkshire Assize Cases (LR-E&W)--Assize.
1v. (1811). MMP   170

Bartram, William (TOS-2)--.... Travels through North and
South Carolina, Georgia, East & West Florida, the
Cherokee country, the extensive territories of the
Muscogulges, or Creek confederacy, and the country
of the Chactaws; ... Philadelphia, printed by James
& Johnson, 1791.   5.95   LoC   171

Bascom, Frances Ridgeway (PH-52)--An investigation of
some aspects of strength and range of motion beyond
180 degrees extension of the knee in college women.
1956. Thesis (Ph.D.), Univ. of Oregon. 83p.
1.25   O   172

Baskett, James Newton (S-B4)--"At you-all's house;"
a Missouri nature story ... New York, Macmillan
Co., 1898. xi, 346 p. 3.95   LoC   173

Batt-Biley--The English ancestry of the families of Batt
and Biley   By James H. Lea. Boston, 1897. 28p.
.80 GML   174

Bautz, Conrad Andrew (HE-47)--Mouth (oral) temperature
changes associated with cigarette, cigar, and pipe
smoking. 1957. Thesis (M.S.), Univ. of Illinois.
52p. 1.15 O   175

Baxter, Andrew (BC-4)--Enquiry into the nature of the
human soul. 1733. 4.95 LoC   176

Bayard, Ferdinand Marie (TOS-3)--Voyage dans
l'interieur des Etats- Unis,... pendant l'été de 1791.
Paris, Chez Cocheris, 1797. 5.95 LoC   177

Bayne, Charles Joseph (S-B4)--The water-spirit's bride
and other poems. New York, J.B. Alden, ...116p.
3.95   LoC   178

Beach--Treatment of ecclesiastics in the French fabliaux
of the Middle Ages. 2.10 KU   179

Beach, J.W.--Romantic view of poetry. 2.00 SM   180

Beal, Gladys Birdice (PE-367)--Reasons for the selection
of certain physical education activities by women students
of the Ohio State University. 1957. Thesis (M.A.),
Ohio State Univ. 61p. 1.05 O   181

Bean, Robert, Expedition (P&R-2)--Letter from Dr.
James S. Craig, ... dated Santa Fe, New Mexico,
Jan. 2, 1831. 5.95 LoC   182

Beattie, James (BC-4)--Dissertations, moral and critical.
1783.   2v. 4.95   each   LoC   183

--------(BC-4)--Elements of moral science. 1790-93.
2v. 4.95 each   LoC   184

--------(BC-4)--An essay on the nature and immutability
of truth in opposition to sophistry and scepticism.
1776. 4.95   LoC   185

--------BC-4)--An essay on truth. 1770.   4.95 LoC 186

--------(BC-4)--Essays. On poetry and music. On
laughter. On the utility of classical learning. 1776.
4.95   LoC   187

--------(BC-4)--Evidences of the Christian religion.
1786. 4.95   LoC   188

Beaujour, Louis Auguste Félix, Baron de (TOS-3)--
Apercu des Etats-Unis, au commencement du XIXe
siecle, depuis 1800 jusqu'en 1810, ... Paris,
L.G. Michaud, imprimeur [etc.], 1814. 5.95 LoC 189

Beavan & Walford (LR-E&W)--Railway. 1v. (1846).
MMP   190

Bebber, Ruth Elizabeth (PH-57)--The relative influence
of the activity of artificial and breast feeding on the
growth and development of the malar prominences of
the face. 1956. Thesis (Ph.D.), Univ. of Southern
California. 132p. 1.65   O   191

Beccher, J.J.--Oedipus Chymicus Seu Institutiones
Chymicae. Neue Ausgabe. Frankfurt a.M., 1716.
Nr. 59-62.   MK   192

Beckford, William (BC-4)--Acemia, descriptive and sentimental novel. 1797. 2v. 4.95 each LoC   193

--------(BC-4)--Biographical memoirs of extraordinary
painters. 1780. 4.95   LoC   194

Berquin-Duvallon (TOS-3)--Vue de la colonie espagnole
  du Mississippi, ou des provinces de Louisiane et
  Floride Occidentale; ... Paris, Imprimerie expedi-
  tive, 1803. 5.95 LoC   221

Bertezén, Salvatore--Principj di musica teorico-prattica.
  Roma, 1780. 2.25 UR   222

Beurhusius, Friedrich--Erotematum mvsicae librie dvo.
  Noribergae, 1580. 1.00 UR   223

Bigelow, John (P&R-1)--Memoir of the life and public
  services of John Charles Fremont. 5.95 LoC   224

Bingley, William (TOS-2)--Travels in North America,
  from modern writers. ... London, printed for
  Harvey & Darton, 1821. 5.95 LoC   225

Binkerd, Adam D. (KC-12)--Pictorial guide to the Mammoth
  Cave, Kentucky. ... Cincinnati, Press of G.P. Houston,
  1888. 112p. 2.72 LoC   226

Birch, Thomas (BC-4)--Life of Dr. John Tillotson.
  1752. 4.95 LoC   227

Birkbeck, Morris (TOS-1)--Notes on a journey in America,
  from the coast of Virginia to the territory of Illinois.
  ... Philadelphia, published by Caleb Richardson,
  ... 1817. 5.95 LoC   228

Bittleston, Chamber Cases (LR-E&W)--King's Bench.
  1v. (1883-84). MMP   229

Bittleston, Wise & Parnell (LR-E&W)--Magistrates.
  5v. (1844-50). MMP   230

Blackburne, Francis (BC-4)--Remarks on Johnson's
  Life of Milton. 1780. 4.95 LoC   231

Blackerby (LR-E&W)--Magistrates. 1v. (1505-1734).
  MMP   232

Blacklock, Thomas (BC-4)--The Graham: an heroic
  ballad. 1774. 4.95 LoC   233

--------(BC-4)--Poems on several occasions. 1746.
  4.95 LoC   234

18

Blackmore, Richard (BC-4)--Alfred, an epic poem in twelve books. 1723. 4.95 LoC   235

--------(BC-4)--Creation, a philosophical poem. 1712. 4.95 LoC   236

--------(BC-4)--The nature of man, a poem in three books. 1711. 4.95 LoC   237

--------(BC-4)--Redemption, a divine poem. 1722. 4.95 LoC   238

Blackwell, Thomas (BC-4)--Ratio sacra; or, an appeal unto the rational world. 1710. 4.95 LoC   239

--------(BC-4)--Schema sacrum; or, a sacred scheme of natural and revealed religion. 1710. 4.95 LoC   240

Blair, Hugh (BC-4)--A critical dissertation on the poems of Ossian. 1763. 4.95 LoC   241

Blanchet, Augustin Maglorius Alexandre (P&R-2)-- Mission de Walla-Walla. [also included with Association de la Propagation de la Foi] 5.95 LoC   242

--------(P&R-2)--Voyage de L'Eveque de Walla-Walla. [also included with Association de la Propagation de la Foi] 5.95 LoC   243

Blanchet, Francois Norbert (P&R-2)--Memoire presente a la S. Congregation de la Propagande sur le Territoire de l'Oregon. [also included with Association de la Propagation de la Foi] 5.95 LoC   244

--------(P&R-2)--Mission de la Colombie. [also included with Association de la Propagation de la Foi] 5.95 LoC245

Blane, William Newnham (TOS-2)--An excursion through the United States and Canada during the years 1822-23. ... London, printed for Baldwin, Cradock, & Joy, 1824. 5.95 LoC   246

Bleeker, Pieter--Atlas Ichthyologique des Indes Neer- landaises (1862-78). 9v. 41.00 F   247

Bliss, Edward (P&R-1)--A brief history of the news gold
   regions of Colorado Territory; together with hints
   and suggestions to intending emigrants. 5.95 LoC   248

Blodget, Lorin, 1823 (AP-1)--The commercial and financial strength of the United States, as shown in the
   balances of foreign trade and the increased production
   of staple articles. Philadelphia, King & Baird,
   printers, 1864. 39p. 2.45 LoC   249

Blood. (1959-   ). 7.50 per vol.   F   250

Blowe, Daniel (TOS-2)--A geographical, historical,
   commerical, and agricultural view of the United States
   of America; ... London, Edwards & Knibb;
   Liverpool, W. Grapel, 1820. 5.95 LoC   251

Blum, Harold Francis--Photodynamic action and diseases
   caused by light. 1941. ACS monograph no. 85.
   9.50 MXT   252

Bock, Hieronymus, 1498-1554 (HS-1)--Hieronymi
   Tragi, De stirpivm, maxime earvm, qvae in Germania
   nostra nascvntur, usitatis nomenclaturis, proprijsq
   differentijs, neq non temperaturis ac facultatibus,
   commentariorum libri tres ... [Argentorati,
   Excudebat V. Rihelius, 1551] 1200p. illus. 14.69
   LoC   253

Bockman, Theodore, Jr. (PE-384)--The correlation of
   thirty-seven tests with the 100 yard drop-off tests in
   swimming. ... 1951. Thesis (M.S.), Univ. of
   Illinois. 57p. 1.15 O   254

Bohun (LR-E&W)--Election. 1v. (1628-99). MMP   255

Boker, George H. --Plays and poems. 3rd ed. 2v.
   5.00 SM   256

Bolduc, Jean-Baptiste Zacharie (P&R-2)--Mission de la
   Colombie. 5.95 LoC   257

Bolt, Richard (BC-4)--A new dictionary of trade and
   commerce. 1756 4.95 LoC   258

Bolton, Herbert E., ed. (TOS-1)--Arrendondo's historical proof of Spain's title to Georgia. Berkeley, Calif., Univ. of Calif. Press, 1925. 5.95 LoC 259

Bolzius (or Boltzius), John Martin (TOS-4)--An extract of the journals of Mr. Commissary Von Reck ... and the Rev. Mr. Bolzius. London, M. Downing, 1734. 5.95 LoC 260

Boner, John Henry (S-B3)--Whispering pines. New York, Brentano Bros; ... 1883. ...167p. 3.25 LoC 261

      Bonner, Sherwood--See McDowell, Mrs. Katherine Sherwood (Bonner)

Bonrepos, Chevalier de (TOS-1)--Description du Mississippi, le nombre des villes & colonies établies par les Francois, ... Ecrite de Mississippi en France, à mademoiselle D---. Imprimé à Rouen, se vend a Paris... 1720. 5.95 LoC 262

      Borch, Oluf--See Borrichius, Olaus

Borden, William (TOS-1)--An address to the Inhabitants of North Carolina; occasioned by the difficult circumstances the Government seems to labour under, for Want of a Medium, or something to answer in lieu of Money; ... Williamsburg [Va.] printed by Wm. Parks, 1746. 5.95 LoC 263

Borrichius, Olaus--De Ortu et Progressu Chemiae Dissertatio. Kopenhagen, 1668. Nr. 51-53. MK 264

Bossu, Jean Barnard (TOS-1)--Nouveau voyages aux Indies occidentales; Paris, Le Jay, ... 1768. 5.95 LoC 265

      Boston Athenaeum. Catalogue--See Catalogue of the Boston Athenaeum.

Bottrigari, Ercole--Il desiderio overo. Venetia, 1594. 1.00 UR 266

Bowles, Samuel (P&R-1)--Across the continent; a summer's journey to the Rocky Mountains, the Mormons, and the Pacific States, ... 5.95 LoC 267

Bowling Green and Warren county immigration society,
Bowling Green, Kentucky, Park City Daily Times
Print, 1885. 54p. 2.50   LoC   268

Bowman, Mary Olive (PSY-106)--The relationship
between student and parent attitudes and skills of
fifth grade children. 1958   Thesis (Ph.D.), State
Univ. of Iowa. 166p. 1.65 O   269

Bownas, Samuel (TOS-4)--An account of the life, travels
and Christian experiences in the work of the ministry
of Samuel Bownas. London,   printed by Luke Hinde,
1756. 5.95   LoC   270

Boyer, Abel (BC-4)--The History of King William III.
1702. 4.95   LoC   271

--------(BC-4)--The Theatre of Honour and Nobility.
1729. 4.95 LoC   272

Boyle, John (HE-48)--Teacher behaviors in pupil medical emergencies. 1957. Thesis (Ed.D.), Stanford
Univ. 103p. 1.40   O   273

Boyle, Mrs. Virginia (Frazer) (S-B4)--The other side,
an historic poem. Cambridge,   Printed at the Riverside Press, 1893. ...64p. 3.95   LoC   274

Boynton,   Charles Brandon & T.B. Mason (P&R-1)--
A journey through Kansas; with sketches of
Nebraska. 5.95 LoC   275

Boyse,   Samuel (BC-4)--An impartial history of the late
Rebellion in 1745. 1748. 4.95   LoC   276

--------(BC-4)--Poems. 1757. 4.95 LoC   277

Brackenridge, Henry Marie (P&R-1, also OV-A2,
TOS-1)--Views of Louisiana, together with a journal
of a voyage up the Missouri River, in 1811. Pittsburgh,
printed & pub. by Cramer, Spear & Eichbaum, ...
1814.   5.95   LoC   278

Brackett, Albert Gallatin (P&R-2)--History of the
United States Cavalry, from the formation of the
Federal Government to the 1st of June, 1863. 5.95
LoC   279

Bracton's Note Book (LR-E&W)--King's Bench. 3v.
(1218-40). MMP   280

Bradbrook, M.C.--Themes and conventions of
Elizabethan tragedy. 2.00 SM   281

Bradbury, John (P&R-1, TOS-1)--Travels in the interior
of America, in the years 1809-11; ... and containing
remarks and observations useful to persons emigrating
to those countries. Liverpool, printed for the author,
by Smith & Galway, ... 1817. 5.95 LoC   282

Brademas, David James (RC-34)--The leisure time
interests of fifty delinquent boys prior to commitment
to the Illinois State Training School for Boys at St.
Charles, Ill. 1955. Thesis (M.S.), Univ. of
Illinois. 145p. 1.65   O   283

Bramlette, Thomas Elliott, 1817 (KC-10)--Speech ...
to ratify the nomination of Gen. George B. McClellan
for president, and George H. Pendleton for vice-
president of the U.S. (Frankfort, Ky., Osborne &
Co.), 1864. 15p. 2.50 LoC   284

Bramston, James (BC-4)--The Art of Politicks; in
imitation of Horace's Art of Poetry. 1729. 4.95
LoC   285

--------(BC-4)--The man of taste, Occasioned by an
epistle of Mr. Pope's on that subject. 1733. 4.95
LoC   286

Brander, G.F.--Beschreibung eines neuerfundenen
Distanzenmessers aus einer Station fur Ingenieurs
und Artilleristen. Augsburg, 1781. Nr. 170-171.
MK   287

--------Kurze Beschreibung einer Camera obscurae.
Augsburg, 1769. Nr. 159 MK   288

Bray, Thomas (TOS-4)--Apostolick charity, its nature
and excellence consider'd. In a discourse ... at the
ordination of some Protestant missionaries to be
sent into the plantations. ... London, printed by
W. Downing for W. Hawes, 1698. 5.95 LoC   289

--------(TOS-4)--A memorial, representing the present
state of religion on the continent of North America.
London, printed by Wm. Downing for the author,
1700. 5.95 LoC   290

Brayton, Frederick Charles (PE-431)--A cinemato-
graphical study of the relative horizontal speed of the
outfielder's throw before and after it skips from the
grass. 1959. Thesis (M.S.), State College of
Washington. 43p. 1.15 O   291

Breckinridge, John Cabell, 1821-77--(AP-1)--History
of Gen. John Cabell Breckinridge New York, Knapp
& Co., c1888. 15p. 2.45 LoC   292

Breckinridge, Joseph Cabell, 1842 (A P-1)--Response
of Gen. J.C. Breckinridge at the banquet of the
Society of the Army of the Cumberland, Chattanooga,
Oct. 10, 1900. Cincinnati, Press of the R. Clarke
Co., 1901. 21p.   2.45   LoC   293

Breckinridge, Robert Jefferson (OV-A5)--A discourse
on the formation and development of the American
mind. Delivered before the literary societies of
Lafayette College, at Easton, Pa., on the 20th
Sept. 1837. And now published at their request.
Baltimore, R.J. Matchett, 1837. 40p. 2.50 LoC   294

Brett, Thomas (BC-4)--The divine right of episcopacy.
1718. 4.95   LoC   295

--------(BC-4)--A sermon on the honour of the Christian
priesthood. 1712.   4.95   LoC   296

--------(BC-4)--A sermon on the remission of sins
according to the scripture and doctrine of the Church
of England. 3d. ed. 1715. 4.95 LoC   297

Brewer, J.--The relations of the English Baptists with
New England in the seventeenth century. Thesis
(B.D.). 1.11.6   MMe   298

Brewster, George (OV-A5)--Lectures on education.
Columbus, Printed for the author, by J. Bailhache,
1833. 359p. 5.94 LoC   299

Brewerton, George Douglas (P&R-2)--A ride with Kit
Carson through the Great American Desert and the
Rocky Mountains. 5.95 LoC   300

Brickell, John (TOS-4)--The natural history of North
Carolina. With an account of the trade, manners,
and customs of the Christian and Indian inhabitants.
Illus. Dublin, James Carson for the author, 1737.
5.95 LoC   301

Brijon, C.R.--L'Apollon moderne, ou le development
intellectuel par les sons de la musique. Lyon, 1782.
2.25 UR   302

Brion de la Tour, Louis (TOS-1)--Almanach intéressant
dans les circonstances presentes. Description abrégée
des Etats Unis de l'Amérique; ... Paris, Desnos
[1780] 5.95 LoC   303

Brissenden, P.F.--The I.W.W.; a study of American
syndicalism. 2d ed. 3.60 SM   304

Brissot de Warville, Jacques Pierre (TOS-3)--Nouveau
voyage dans les Etats-Unis de l'Amerique septentrionale,
fait en 1788; ... Paris, Buisson, 1791. 3v. 5.95
each LoC   305

Bristed, John (OV-A5)--The resources of the United
States of America; or, A view of the agricultural,
commercial, manufacturing,financial, political,
literary, moral and religious capacity and character
of the American people. New York, published by
James Eastburn & Co. ... 1818. 505p. 7.54 LoC 306

Bristow, W. (BC-4)--The genuine account of the life
and writings of Eugene Aram. 1759. 4.95 LoC   307

British Culture on Microcards. Group 3 (English literature: Reference works and collections). Group price,
2.95 per vol. LoC   308
The titles in this series are:
    Aubrey, J.--Miscellanies upon various subjects.
    Bale, J.--Scriptorvm illustriu Maioris Brytannie, ...

Cattermole, R.--Literature of the Church of
England ...
Eyre-Todd, G., ed.--Early Scottish poetry; ...
Eyre-Todd, G., ed.--Medieval Scottish poetry.
Eyre-Todd, G., ed.--Scottish ballad poetry.
Eyre-Todd, G., ed.--Scottish poetry of the 18th
century.
Eyre-Todd, G., ed.--Scottish poetry of the 17th
century.
Eyre-Todd, G., ed.--Scottish poetry of the 16th
century.
Farr, E., ed.--Select poetry, chiefly sacred, ...
Fuller, T.--History of the worthies of England.
Gillow, J.--...Biographical dictionary of the English
Catholics, ...
Haslewood, J., ed.--Ancient critical essays upon
English poets and poesy.
Hazlitt, W.C.--Prefaces, dedications, epistles ...
Hazlitt, W.C., comp.--Remains of the early popular
poetry of England.
Irving, D.--Lives of Scottish writers.
Irving, D.--Lives of the Scottish poets. ...
Laing, D., ed. -- Early popular poetry of Scotland ...
Tanner, T.--Bibliotheca britannico-hibernica: ...
Walker, H.--Three centuries of Scottish literature.
Warton, T.--History of English poetry from the
12th to the close of the 16th century ...
Wood, A.A.--Athenae oxonienses ...

British Culture on Microcards. Group 4 (A selection of
books relating to 18th century English culture). Group
price, 2.95 per vol. LoC   309
The titles in this series are:
Abercromby, P.--The martial achievements of the
Scots nation.
Aikin, J.--Essay on the plan and character of
Thompson's Seasons.
Alexis; or, The young adventurer.
Ames, J.-- Typographical Antiquities.
Amhurst, N.--Terrae Filius, ...
Amory, T.--Life of John Buncle, ...
Amory, T.--Memoirs containing the lives of several
ladies of Great Britain.
Anderson, J.--Selectus diplomatum ...

Anderson, J.--Account of the present state of the
  Hebrides ...
Anderson, J. [1739-1808]--Essays relating to agri-
  culture and rural affairs.
Anderson, J. [1739-1808]--Interest of Great Britain
  with regard to her American colonies considered.
Anderson, R.--Life of Samuel Johnson.
Annet, P.--Collection of the tracts of a certain free
  enquirer.
Annet, P.--Resurrection of Jesus considered.
Arbuthnot, A., pseud.--The life adventures ... of
  Simon Lord Loval.
Arbuthnot, A., pseud.--Memoirs of ... Miss Jenny
  Cameron.
Arbuthnot, J.--Miscellaneous works.
Arbuthnot, J.--The art of preserving health.
Armstrong, J.--Benevolence.
Armstrong, J.--A Day.
Armstrong, J.--The Economy of Love.
Armstrong, J.--Sketches or essays on various subjects.
Armstrong, J.--An epistle to a young critic.
Ayliffe, J.--The Ancient and present state of the
  University of Oxford.
Ayliffe, J.--The case of Dr. Ayliffe at Oxford.
B., T.--A criticism by T.B. on the New Sophonisba.
Bage, R.--Barham Downs.
Bage, R.--The fairsyrian.
Bage, R.--Hermsprong; ...
Bage, R.--James Wallace.
Bage, R.--Man as he is.
Bage, R.--Mount Henneth.
Baker, D.E.--The companion to the play-house.
Baker, H.--Original poems.
Baker, T.--Reflections upon learning, ...
Balguy, J.--A collection of tracts, ...
Balguy, J.--Essay on redemption.
Bamthylde, J.C.--Sixteen sonnets.
Barber, M.--Poems on several occasions.
Barclay, R.--A modest and serious address ...
Barclay, J.--An examination of Mr. Kenrick's review..
Baxter, A.--Enquiry into the nature of the human soul.
Beattie, J.--Dissertations, moral and critical.
Beattie, J.--Elements of moral science.
Beattie, J.--Essay on the nature and immutability of
  truth ...

Beattie, J.--An essay on truth.
Beattie, J.--Essays. On poetry and music.
Beattie, J.--Evidences of the Christian religion.
Beckford, W.--Acemia, ...
Beckford, W.--Biographical memoirs of extraordinary
  painters.
Beckford, W.--Dreams, waking thoughts, and incidents.
Beckford, W.--Modern novel writing, ...
Beckford, W.--Story of Al Raoui.
Bennett, B.--On the truth, inspiration and usefulness
  of the sacred scriptures.
Bentley, R.--The case of Trinity College in Cambridge.
Bentley, R.--Dr. Bentley's proposals to print a
  new edition of the Greek testament, ...
Bentley, R.--The present state of Trinity College ...
Bentley, R.--Proposals to print a new edition of the
  Greek Testament.
Bentley, R.--Remarks upon a late discourse of free-
  thinking.
Bentley, R.--Sermon upon Popery.
Bentley, R.--Sermon preached before King George.
Benson, G.--The reasonableness of the Christian
  religion.
Birch, T.--Life of Dr. John Tillotson.
Blackburne, F.--Remarks on Johnson's Life of Milton.
Blacklock, T.--The Graham: an heroic ballad.
Blacklock, T.--Poems on several occasions.
Blackmore, R.--Alfred, an epic poem ...
Blackmore, R.--Creation, a philosophical poem.
Blackmore, R.--The nature of man, ...
Blackmore, R.--Redemption, a divine poem.
Blackwell, T.--Ratio Sacra; ...
Blackwell, T.--Schema sacrum; ...
Blair, H.--A critical dissertation on the poems of Ossian.
Bolt, R.--A new dictionary of trade and commerce.
Boyer, A.--History of King William III.
Boyer, A.--The Theatre of Honour and Nobility.
Boyse, S.--Impartial history of the late Rebellion in
  1745.
Boyse, S.-- Poems
Bramston, J.--The art of Politicks; ...
Bramston, J.--The man of taste, ...
Brett, T.--The divine right of episcopacy.
Brett, T.--A sermon on the honour of the Christian
  priesthood.

Brett, T. --A sermon on the remission of sins ...
Bristow, W. --The genuine account of the life and
    writings ofEugene Aram.
The British Theatre: ...
Brooke, H. --The case of the Roman Catholics of
    Ireland.
Brooke, H. --The Earl of Essex.
Brooke, H. --Fables for the female sex.
Brooke, H. --The farmer's letters to the Protestants
    of Ireland.
Brooke, H. --The fool of quality, ...
Brooke, H. --Gustavus Vasa, ...
Brooke, H. --The interest of Ireland considered.
Brooke, H. --Juliet Grenville.
Brooke, H. --Redemption.
Brooke, H. --The spirit of party.
Brooke, H. --Tryal of cause of Roman Catholics.
Brooke, H. --Universal beauty.
Brown, T., of Shifnal--Works.
Browne, I.H. --Poems ...
Browne, P. --Procedure, extent and limits of the
    human understanding.
Browne, P. --Things divine and supernatural ...
Browne, S. --Defense of the religion of nature.
Browne, S. --A fit rebuke.
Browne, S. --Hymns and spiritual songs.
Brownell, R.C. --Tempera Thomsoni in latino versu
    raddita.
Brounsmith, J. --The dramatic time-piece; ...
Bruce, M. --Poems on several occasions.
Bryant, J. --Observations on the poems of T. Rowley, ..
Budgell, E., --A letter to a friend in the country.
Budgell, E. --A letter to Mr. Law ...
Budgell, E. --Memoirs ... particularly Charles, Earl
    of Orrery.
Burton, J.--...Journal of the ... young Chevalier, ...
Byrom, J. --Miscellaneous poems.
Byssle, E. --The art of English poetry.

British Journal of Educational Psychology. 1931-1956.
    Each year, 2.10; complete set, 62.0 MMe   310

British Journal of Plastic Surgery. 1957. 3.0 MMe   311

The British Theatre (BC-4)--Containing the lives of the
English dramatic poets with an account of all their
plays. 1750. 4.95 LoC   312

Das brittische reich in America, sammt den eroberten
Canada mit denem wichtigen inseln Gadaloupe, Martinique
und andern se-platzen (TOS-4), oder: Kurzgefasste
Beschreibung der englandischen pflanzstadte ...
Sorau, Gottlob Hebold, 1761. 5.95 LoC   313

Brockway, Thomas (TOS-1)--The European traveller in
America. ... Hartford, printed by Hudson & Goodwin,
1785. 5.95 LoC   314

Bromiley, Frances (ACRL-117)--The history and organi-
zation of the Franklin D. Roosevelt Library, Hyde
Park, New York. 1959. Thesis (M.S. in L.S.),
Western Reserve Univ. 1.50 UR   315

Brooke (LR-E&W)-- Ecclesiastical. 1v. (1850-72).
MMP   316

Brooke, Henry (BC-4)--The case of the Roman Catholics
of Ireland. 1760. 4.95 LoC   317

--------(BC-4)--The Earl of Essex. A tragedy. 1761.
4.95 LoC   318

--------(BC-4)--Fables for the female sex, by E. Moore
and H. Brooke. 1744. 4.95 LoC   319

--------(BC-4)--The farmer's letters to the Protestants of
Ireland. 1760. 4.95 LoC   320

--------(BC-4)--The fool of quality, or The history of
Henry, Earl of Moreland. 1766-70. 5v. 4.95
each LoC   321

--------(BC-4)--Gustavus Vasa, the deliverer of his country.
A tragedy. 1739. 4.95 LoC   322

--------(BC-4)--The interest of Ireland considered.
1759. 4.95 LoC   323

--------(BC-4)--Juliet Grenville. 1774. 3v. 4.95 each
LoC   324

--------(BC-4)--Redemption. 1771. 4.95   LoC   325

--------(BC-4)--The spirit of party. 1753-54. 4.95
   LoC   326

--------(BC-4)--Tryal of cause of Roman Catholics.
   1761. 4.95   LoC   327

--------(BC-4)--Universal beauty. 1735. 4.95 LoC   328

Brooks, John (TOS-3)--Life and times ... in which are
   contained a history of the great revival in Tennessee;
   ... Nashville, Nashville Christian Advocate Office,
   1848. 5.95 LoC   329

Brown, Gaydena Marlene (PE-432)--The relationship between body types and static posture of young adult women
   at the State College of Washington as related with body
   alignment and the gravital line at the base of support.
   1959. Thesis (M.S.), State College of Washington.
   52p. 1.15   O   330

Brown, George (AP-1)--The American war and slavery.
   Speech at the anniversary meeting of the Anti-slavery
   Soc. of Canada. Manchester, Union & Emancipation
   Soc., 1863. 16p. 2.45 LoC   331

Brown, John, 1800, defendant (AP-1)--The life, trial and
   conviction of Capt. John Brown, known as "Old
   Brown of Ossawatomie," with a full account of the attempted
   insurrection at Harper's Ferry. New York, R.M.
   DeWitt, c1859. ...108p. 2.45 LoC   332

Brown, John Henry (S-B4)--History of Texas, from
   1685 to 1892. St. Louis, L.E. Daniell (c1892-93).
   2v. 3.95 LoC   333

Brown, Joseph M., 1851 (AP-1)--The mountain campaigns
   in Georgia; or, War scenes on the W. & A. Buffalo,
   N.Y., Art-Printing works of Matthews, Northrop &
   Co., 1886. ...51p. 2.45 LoC   334

Brown, Katherine M. (PE-409)--The work of Mary
   Wigman. 1955. Thesis (M.S.), Univ. of Utah.
   70p. 1.15   O   335

Brown, Robert J. & Riley, Douglas R. (PE-368)--
The effect of weight training on leg strength
and the vertical jump. 1957. Thesis (M.S.),
Springfield College. 77p. 1.05 O   336

Brown, Samuel R. (TOS-3)--The western gazetteer;
or, emigrant's directory, containing a geographical
description of the western states and territories;
... Auburn, N.Y., printed by H.C. Southwick,
1817. 5.95 LoC   337

Brown, Tarleton (TOS-4)--Memoirs ... with a
preface and notes, by C.I. Bushnell . New York,
privately printed, 1862. 5.95 LoC   338

Brown, Thomas (KC-8)--Brown's three years in the
Kentucky prisons, from May 30, 1854 to May 18,
1857. Indianapolis, Courier Co. Print, 1857.
21p. 2.50 LoC   339

Brown, Tom, of Shifnal (BC-4)--Works. 1720.
4v. 4.95 each LoC   340

Browne, Chad--Chad Brown of Providence, R.I.
and four generations of his descendants. By Wm.
B. Browne. With typewritten index. Boston, 1926.
31p. 1.10 GML   341

Browne, Isaac Hawkins (BC-4)--Poems upon various
subjects Latin and English. Ed. by his son.
1768. 4.95 LoC   342

Browne, J. Ross (P&R-2)--A tour through America.
5.95 LoC   343

Browne, Peter (BC-4)-- Procedure, extent, and limits
of the human understanding. 1728. 4.95 LoC   344

--------(BC-4)--Things divine and supernatural conceived
by analogy with things natural and human. 1733.
4.95 LoC   345

Browne, Simon (BC-4)--Defense of the religion of
nature. 1732. 4.95 LoC   346

--------(BC-4)--A fit rebuke. 1732. 4.95 LoC 347

--------(BC-4)--Hymns and spiritual songs. 1720.
4.95 LoC 348

Brownell, R.C. (BC-4)--Tempera Thomsoni in latino
versu raddita. 1795. 4.95 LoC 349

Brounsmith, J. (BC-4)--The dramatic time-piece;
or perpetual monitor. 1767. 4.95 LoC 350

Bruce, Michael (BC-4)--Poems on several occasions.
1770. 4.95 LoC 351

Brumbach, Wayne Baker (PH-58)--Changes in the serum
cholesterol levels of male college students who
participated in a vigorous physical exercise program.
1959. Thesis (Ph.D.), Univ. of Oregon. 63p.
1.15 O 352

Brunschwig, Hieronymus, ca.1450-ca.1510 (HS-1)--
Thesavrvs pavpervm: einn fürltrefliche vnd volkomne
Haussapoteck. Franckfurt, C. Ege [nolff, 1537].
76 1. illus.3.43 LoC 353

Bryant, Edwin (P&R-1)--What I saw in California;
being the journal of a tour, by the emigrant route
and South Pass of the Rocky Mountains, ... in the
years 1846-47. 5.95 LoC 354

Bryant, J. (BC-4)--Observations on the poems of
T. Rowley, in which the authenticity of those
poems is ascertained. 1781. 4.95 LoC 355

Buck (LR-E&W)--Bankruptcy. 1v. (1816-20). MMP 356

Budgell, Eustace (BC-4)--A letter to a friend in the
country. 1721. 4.95 LoC 357

--------(BC-4)--A letter to Mr. Law on his arrival
in England. 1721. 4.95 LoC 358

--------(BC-4)--Memoirs of the lives and characters of
the illustrious family of the Broyles, particularly
Charles, Earl of Orrery. 1737. 4.95 LoC 359

Buechler, Johann Ulrich (TOS-3)--Land--und Seereisen
eines St. Gallischen Kantonsbürgers nach Nord-
Amerika und Westindien, über Amsterdam nach
Baltimore, ... in den Jahren 1816-18. ... St.
Gallen, Zollikofer und Zublin. 5.95 LoC   360

Buell Record--Record of the family of Hon. Will H.
Buell, his ancestors and descendants. By Jonathan
S. Buell. 109p. 1.40 GML   361

Bullock, William (OV-A5)--Sketch of a journey through
the Western states of North America, from New
Orleans ... to New York, in 1827. London, J.
Miller, 1827. 135p. 3.48 LoC   362

--------(TOS-1)--Virginia impartially examined, and
left to publick view, to be considered by all
judicious and honest men. ... London, printed
by John Hammond, 1649. 5.95 LoC   363

Bulow, Dietrich (i.e. Adam Heinrich Dietrich,
freiherr von) (TOS-2)--Der freistaat von Nordamerika in seinem neusten zustand, ... Berlin, J.F.
Unger, 1797. 2v. 5.95 each LoC   364

Bundgaard, Axel Christensen (PE-410)--Physical
education for boys in selected Iowa high schools.
1958. Thesis (Ph.D.), State Univ. of Iowa.
126p. 1.65 O   365

Burk, J.S.--History of Virginia. 4v. 17.50 SM   366

Burke, Roger K. (PH-53)--Relationships between physical performance and warm-up procedures of vary-
ing intensity and duration. 1957. Thesis (Ph.D.),
Univ. of Southern California. 159p. 1.50   O   367

Burnyeat, John (TOS-1)--The truth exalted in the
writings of ... John Burnyeat ... London, T.
Northcott, 1691. 5.95 LoC   368

Burrow (LR-E&W)--Settlement. 1v. (1732-76). MMP 369

Burton, John (BC-4)--A genuine and true journal of the
most miraculous escape of the young Chevalier from
the battle of Culloden to his landing in France. 1749.
4.95 LoC   370

Burton, Richard Francis (P&R-1)--The City of the Saints
and across the Rocky Mountains to California.
5.95 LoC   371

Butel-Dumont, Georges Marie (TOS-2)--Histoire et
commerce des colonies angloises, dans l'Amérique
septentrionale, ... A Londres, ... Dessaint,
Pissot, Lambert, 1755. 5.95 LoC   372

Butler, James R.M.--The passing of the Great Reform
Bill. 3.50 SM   373

Buttrick, Tilly (OV-A5)--Voyages, travels and
discoveries ... Boston, printed for the author,
1831. 58p.   2.63 LoC   374

Buttstett, Johann Heinrich--Ut, re, mi, fa, sol, la,
tota musica et harmonia aeterna ... Erffurt
[1717] 3.00 UR   375

Byrd, William (TOS-1)--History of the dividing line,
run in the year 1728. In William Byrd, The
Westover mss. ... Petersburg [Va.] printed by
E. &J.C. Ruffin, 1841. 5.95 LoC   376

--------(TOS-1)--A journey to the land of Eden in
the year 1733. Also list of company of all sorts
and account of the distances of places. In William
Byrd, The Westover mss. ... Petersburg [Va.]
printed by E. &J.C. Ruffin, 1841. 5.95 LoC   377

--------(TOS-1)--A progress to the mines, in the year
1732. In William Byrd, The Westover mss. ...
Petersburg [Va.] printed by E. &J.C. Ruffin, 1841.
5.95 LoC   378

Byrom, John (BC-4)--Miscellaneous poems. Manchester,
1773. 2v. 4.95 each LoC   379

Byssle, Edward (BC-4)--The art of English poetry.
3d ed. 1702. 4.95 LoC   380

C

Cababe & Ellis (LR-E&W)--Queen's bench. 1v (1882-
85). MMP   381

Cabeza de Vaca, Alvar Núñez (TOS-1)--Journey of
Alvar Núñez Cabeza de Vaca and his companions from
Florida to the Pacific, 1528-1536; tr. from his own
narrative by Fanny Bandelier, together with the report
of Father Marcos of Nizza and a letter from the vice-
roy Mendoza; ed., with an introd. by Ad. F. Bandelier
... New York, A.S. Barnes & Co., 1905. 5.95 LoC 382

The Cactus and Succulent Journal. 1957. 1.0 MMe   383

Cairnes, John Elliott, 1823 (AP-1)--The revolution in
America. 2d ed. Dublin, Hodges, Smith & Co.,
1863? 44p. 2.45 LoC   384

Caldecott (LR-E&W)--Magistrates Cases. 1v. (1776-85).
MMP   385

Caldwell, William--Wm. Coaldwell, Caldwell, or
Coldwell of England, Mass., Conn. and Canada.
Historical sketch of the family and record of his
descendants. By Charles T. Caldwell. Washington,
D.C., 1910. 82p. 1.10 GML   386

Caldwell Fam.--A branch of the Caldwell family tree;
a record of Thompson Baxter Caldwell and his wife,
Mary Ann (Ames) of West Bridgewater, Mass. By
Charles T. Caldwell. Washington, 1906. 18p.
.80 GML   387

Caldwell Records--John and Sarah (Dillingham) Cald-
well, Ipswich, Mass., and their descendants. By
Augustine Caldwell. Boston, 1873. 80p. 1.10
GML   388

Callahan, J.M.--Diplomatic history of the Southern
Confederacy. 2.50 SM   389

Camp, George King (S-B4)--Shadows. San Francisco,
A.L. Bancroft & Co., 1885. ... 193p. 3.95 LoC 390

Campbell, Albert H. (P&R-2)--Pacific wagon roads.
Letter from the Secretary of the Interior, transmitting
a report ... 5.95 LoC   391

Campbell, John Wilson (OV-A5)--Biographical sketches;
with other literary remains of the late John W. Campbell.
Comp. by his widow. Columbus, O., Printed by
Scott & Gallagher, 1838. 279p. 5.06 LoC   392

Campbell, Lewis Davis, 1811 (AP-1)--Speech ... on
southern aggression, the purposes of the union, and
the comparative effects of slavery and freedom.
Washington, printed and for sale by Buell & Blanchard,
1850. Cover-title. 16p. 2.45 LoC   393

Canavella, Charles A. (AP-1)--Confederate diary of
C.A. Canavella, Co. E 3d Alabama Infantry, 1861-64.
Copy prepared by Hist. Records Survey, WPA, State
Office. Jacksonville, Fla., 1938. 8 1.2.45 LoC   394

Cancer. (1959-   ).   7.50 per vol. F   395

Cancer Research. Vols. 4-8 (1944-48). 45.00 C   396

Cancer Research. (1959-   ). 5.50 per vol.   F   397

Candler, Isaac (TOS-3)--A summary view of
America: comprising a description of the face of the
country, ... London; Edinburgh, T. Cadell; W.
Blackwood, 1824. 5.95 LoC   398

Canonge, L. (S-B3)--Maudit passeport! ou Les infortunes
d'une drogue, vaudeville en un acte. Nouvelle-Orleans,
Imprime par Gaux & Co., 1840. 60p. 3.25 LoC   399

Canter, Th.--Variarum Lectionum libri duo. Antwerpen,
Christoph Plantin, 1574. Nr. 160-61. MK   400

Canticum Canticorum. Nach dem Exemplar der Bayer-
ischen Staatsbibliothek. München. Nr. 165
(Berühmtes Blockbuch mit 16 Doppelholzschnitten).
MK   401

Cardozo, Jacob Newton (S-B3)--Reminiscences of Charleston.
Charleston, J. Walker, printer, 1866. 144p. 3.25
LoC   402

Carey, H.C.--Principles of political economy. 3v.
8.40 SM   403

37

Carey, H.C.--Principles of social sciences. 2v.
9.60 SM   404

Carey, Mathew (TOS-4)--Carey's American pocket atlas:
containing nineteen maps, ... 2d ed. greatly improved
& enl. Philadelphia, printed by H. Sweitzer for
M. Carey, 1801. 5.95 LoC   405

Carissimi, Giovanni Giacomo--Ars cantandi ... Augspurg,
1693. 1.00 UR   406

Carleton, James Henry(P&R-2)--Diary of an excursion
to the ruins of Abo, Quarra, and Gran Quivira, in
New Mexico. 5.95 LoC   407

--------(P&R-2)--The overland route to California.
5.95 LoC   408

Carolina described more fully than heretofore (TOS-4);
being an impartial collection from the several
Relations of that place, ... Dublin, 1684. 5.95 LoC 409

Carolo Bor. Presl.--Tentamen pteridographiae seu
genera filicacearum. 1.5. MMe   410

Carpenter, Rhys--The esthetic basis of Greek art of
the 5th and 4th centuries B.C. 2.00 SM   411

Carpmael (LR-E&W)--Patent. 3v. (1604-1840). MMP 412

Carrow, Hamerton & Allen (LR E&W)--Magistrates cases.
4v. (1844-51). MMP   413

Cartmell (LR-E&W)--Trade Mark. 1v. (1876-92). MMP414

Cartwright, Peter (TOS-1)--Autobiography ... New York,
Carlton & Porter, 1856. 5.95 LoC   415

Caruthers, William Alexander (S-B4)--A lecture delivered
before the Georgia Historical Society, at the Unitarian
Church, in Savannah, ... 14th March 1843 ...
Savannah, Press of Lock & Davis, 1843. 36p.
3.95 LoC   416

Carver, Jonathan (TOS-2)--The new universal traveller; containing a full and distinct account of all the empires, kingdoms, and states, in the known world. ... London, Robinson, 1779. 5.95   LoC   417

Casas, Bartolomede de las--See B. de las Casas

Cases of Settlements & Removals (LR-E&W)--King's bench.1v. (1685-1733). MMP   418

Casseday, Ben(MFM)--The history of Louisville, from its earliest settlement till the year 1852. 225p. 4.30 LoC   419

Castelman, Richard (TOS-4)--The voyage, shipwreck, and miraculous preservation of Richard Castelman, gent. with a description of the city of Philadelphia, and the country of Pennsylvania. In William Rufus Chetwood, Voyages and adventures ... London, printed for J. Watts, 1726. 5.95 LoC   420

Castiglioni, Luigi, Conte (TOS-1)--Viaggio negli Stati Uniti dell' America Settentrionale, fatto negli anni, 1785, ... 1787. ... Milano, Stamperia di G. Marelli, 1790. 2v. 5.95 each LoC   421

Catalogue of the Boston Athenaeum, 1807-71. proposed, 22.00 F   422

Catalogue of the Peabody Institute. proposed, 65.00 F   423

Cattermole, Richard (BC-3)--The literature of the Church of England indicated in selections from the writings of eminent divines. London, J.W. Parker, 1844. 2v. v1, 5.95; v2, 3.60 LoC   424

Chalkley, Thomas (TOS-4)--A journal or historical account of the life, travels and Christian experiences of that antient, faithful servant of Jesus Christ, ... 2d ed. London, Luke Hinde, 1751. 5.95 LoC   425

Chalmers, Lionel (TOS-2)--An account of the weather and diseases of South Carolina. ... London, printed for E. & C. Dilly, 1776. 5.95 LoC   426

Champigny, Jean, Chevalier de (TOS-1)--La Louisiane
  ensanglantée, avec toutes les particularités de cette
  horrible catastrophe, ... Londres, Aus depens de
  l'editeur, chez Fleury Mesplet, 1773. 5.95 LoC   427

--------(TOS-4)--The present state of the country and
  inhabitants, Europeans and Indians, of Louisiana,
  ... Trans. from the French originals ... by Capt.
  Aylmer, ... London, printed for J. Millam, 1744.
  5.95 LoC   428

Chandless, William (P&R-1)-- A visit to Salt Lake ;
  being a journey across the plains and a residence in
  the Mormon settlements at Utah. 5.95 LoC   429

Chapman, Frederick Morey (RC-28)--The determination
  of the course areas for a graduate curriculum in hospital recreation. 1958. Thesis (D.Rec.), Indiana
  Univ. 138p. 1.50   O   430

Charlevoix, Pierre Francois Xavier de (TOS-1)--Histoire
  et description generale de la Nouvelle France, avec le
  Journal Historique d'un Voyage, ... Paris, chez
  Pierre-Francois Giffart, 1744. 3v. 5.95 each LoC   431

--------(TOS-1)--Journal d'un voyage fait ... dans
  l'Amérique Septentrionale, addressé à Madame la
  Duchesse de Lesdiguières. Vol. V & VI of his
  Histoire et description generale de la Nouvelle
  France, which see. 5.95 LoC   432

Charley's New Practice Cases (LR-E&W)--Practice.
  3v. (1875-81). MMP   433

Chase, Lucien Bonaparte (S-B3)--English serfdom and
  American slavery; or, ourselves--as others see us.
  New York, H. Long & Brother (c1854). ...259p.
  3.25 LoC   434

Chase, Peter S. (AP-1)--Reunion greeting, together with an historical sketch, and a complete descriptive list of the members of Co. I, 2d Regt., Vt.
  vols., in the war for the Union, with final statement
  of the regiment. Brattleboro, Vt., Phoenix Job
  Prtg. Office, 1891. 61p. 2.45 LoC   435

Chemical Abstracts. 1st Decennial Index (1907-1916). ACS   436

Chemical Engineering Progress. Vols. 1-33 (1908-1940). 150.00 C   437

Chesnutt, Charles Waddell (S-B3)--The conjure woman. Boston & New York, Houghton, Mifflin & Co., 1899. ...229p. 3.25 LoC   438

--------(S-B4)--The wife of his youth, and other stories of the color line. With illus. by C.O. DeLand. Boston & New York, Houghton, Mifflin & Co., 1899. ...323p. LoC   439

Chetwood, William Rufus (TOS-1)--The voyages, dangerous adventures and imminent escapes of Capt. Richard Falconer; ... London, W. Chetwood (etc.), 1720. 5.95 LoC   440

Chicago Bar Record. Vols. 1-9 (1910-1926). 4.00 AB   441

Child Study. Vols. 1-31 (1923-1954). 76.00 C   442

Ching, R.C. --A revision of the Chinese and Sikkim-Himalayan dryopteris. 1.10.6 MMe   443

Chiodino, Giovanni Battista--Arte prattica & poetica ... Franckfurt, 1653. 1.00 UR   444

Chitty (LR-E&W)--King's bench. 2v. (1770-1822). MMP   445

Choulant (HS-1)--Graph. Incun., p. 64 no. 17. Schreiber. Die Kraütterbucher des XV und XVI Jahrhunderts, p. xxiv-xxv. 7.65 LoC   446

Christie, Thomas (TOS-1)--A description of Georgia, by a gentleman who has resided there upwards of seven years, ... London, printed for C. Corbett,1741. 5.95 LoC   447

Churchman, John (TOS-1)--An account of the gospel
labours, ... of a faithful minister of Christ, ... To
which is added a short memorial of the life and death
of ... Joseph White, ... Philadelphia, printed by
Joseph Crukshank, ... 1779. 5.95 LoC   448

Claiborne, John Francis Hamtramck (S-B4)--Life and
correspondence of John A. Quitman major-general
U.S.A. and governor of the State of Mississippi.
New York, Harper & Bros., 1860. 2v. 3.95 each
LoC   449

--------(TOS-3)--Life and times of Gen. Sam Dale, the
Mississippi partisan. ... New York, Harper &
Bros., 1860. 5.95 LoC   450

--------(S-B4)--Mississippi, as a province, territory
and state, with biographical notices of eminent citizens.
Vol 1. Jackson, Miss., Power & Barksdale, 1880.
xxii, 545p. 3.95 LoC   451

Clark, Charles M. (P&R-2)--A trip to Pike's Peak
and notes by the way, ... 5.95 LoC   452

Clark, George Rogers (TOS-2)--Memoir. In
William H. English, Conquest of the country north-
west of the river Ohio, 1778-83. And life of
George Rogers Clark. 2v. Indianapolis, Bobbs-
Merrill Co., 1869. 5.95 LoC   453

    Clark, Thomas D., Travels in the Old South--
    See series entries: Travels in the Old South
    or individual entries.

Clark, William (P&R-2)--Letter to his brother, George
Rogers Clark, dated St. Louis, Sept. 23, 1806.
5.95 LoC   454

Clarke, C.B.--A review of the ferns of Northern
India. 1.1 MMe   455

Clarke, David H. (PSY-79)--Social status and mental
health of boys as related to their maturity, structural characteristics and muscular strength. 1959.
Thesis (Ph.D.), Univ. of Oregon. 121p. 1.50 O 456

Clarke, George (TOS-1)--Voyage of George Clarke, Esq., to America. With introd. and notes, by E.B. O'Callaghan. Albany, J. Munsell, 1867. 5.95 LoC   457

Clarke, Margaret C. (PE-385)--A program of physical education in a State Teachers College. 1943. Thesis (Ph.D.), New York Univ. 452p. 3.00 O   458

Clary, Ann Roane (ACRL-104)--A check-list of Richmond, Virginia imprints from 1821 through 1830. 1956. Thesis (M.S. in L.S.), Catholic Univ. of America. 1.50 UR   459

Clay, Cassius Marcellus (KC-14)--Appeal ... to Kentucky and the world. Boston, J.M. Macomber & E.L. Pratt, 1845. 35p. 3.95 LoC   460

Clayton's York Assizes (LR-E&W)--Assize. 1v. (1631-51). MMP   461

Clifford's Southwark (LR-E&W)--Election. 1v. (1796-97). MMP   462

Clower, Mary Alice (PSY-92)--A comparison of college freshmen women of high and low motor ability with regard to selected physical and psychological capacities. 1958. Thesis (Ed.M.), Woman's College, Univ. of North Carolina. 107p. 1.40 O   463

Cobane, Edith (PSY-107)--A comparison of two methods of teaching selected motor skills 1959. Thesis (Ed.D.), Syracuse Univ. 108p. 1.40 O   464

Cobbe, Francis Power, (1822 (AP-1)--The red flag in John Bull's eyes. London, E. Faithfull, 1863. 24p. 2.45 LoC   465

Cobden, Richard, 1804 (AP-1)--Speech ... on the "Foreign enlistment act," in the House of Commons, April 24, 1863. 2d. ed. London, W. Ridgway, 1863. 25p. 2.45 LoC   466

Cobden-Sanderson, T.J., London--A paper read at a meeting of the Art Workers Guild. Doves Press, London, 1906. Nr.140. MK   467

Cockburn & Rowe (LR-E&W)--Election. 1v. (1833).
MMP   468

Cocke, Zitella (S-B3)--A Doric reed. Boston, Copeland & Day, 1895. ix, 91p. 3.25 LoC   469

Coffin, Levi (TOS-3)--Reminiscences of Levi Coffin,
the reputed president of the Underground Railroad;
... Cincinnati, Western Tract Soc. [1876] 5.95
LoC   470

Coke, Hon. Henry John (P&R-1)--A ride over the
Rocky Mountains to Oregon and California. With a
glance at some of the tropical islands, including
the West Indies and the Sandwich Isles.   5.95
LoC   471

Coke, Thomas (TOS-1)--Extracts of the journals ...
comprising several visits to North America and the
West Indies; ... Dublin, printed by R. Napper ...
1816. 5.95 LoC   472

Colby, John (OV-A5)--Life, experiences and travels
... Lowell, Mass., N. Thurston & A. Watson,
1838. 2v. in 1 6.39 LoC   473

Cold Spring Harbor Symposia on Quantitative Biology.
Vols. 11-12 (1943-1947). Per vol., 4.00 C   474

Cole, A.C.--Whig part in the South. 3.50 SM   475

Coleraine, George Hanger, 4th Baron (TOS-2)--The
life, adventures and opinions ... [Ed. by W.
Combe] London, Debrett, 1801. 2v. 5.95
each LoC   476

Colt, Mrs. Miriam Davis (P&R-1)--Went to Kansas;
...account of an ill-fated expedition to that fairy
land, ... 5.95 LoC   477

Coltman (LR-E&W)--Registration. 1v. (1879-85).
MMP   478

Colville, Frances M. (PSY-80)--The learning of motor
skills as influenced by knowledge of general principles of mechanics. 1956. Thesis (Ph.D.), Univ.
of Southern California. 146p. 1.50 O   479

Combs, Leslie, 1793 (KC-14)--Col. Wm. Dudley's
defeat opposite Fort Meigs. May 5th, 1813.
Printed for Wm. Dodge. Cincinnati, Spiller &
Gates, printers, 1869. 13p. 3.95 LoC   480

Common Law Reports (LR-E&W)--King's Bench.
3v. (1853-55). MMP   481

A compendious description of the thirteen colonies, in
British-America (TOS-1). London, printed for
Herman, Strong & Co., 1777. 5.95 LoC   482

A concise historical account of all the British colonies
in North-America (TOS-2), comprehending their
rise, progress, and modern state; ... London,
printed for J. Bew, 1775. 5.95 LoC   483

Confederate Imprints. in prep   LoC   484

Confederate States of America. District courts. South
Carolina (AP-1)--The sequestration cases, before
the Hon. A.G. Magrath. Reported by J. Woodruff.
Charleston, 1861. ... 67p. 2.45 LoC   485

Congressional Globe (1833-1873.) proposed, 500.00 F 486

Congressional Quarterly (published weekly; indexed
quarterly; includes annual Almanac). Backfile,
1945-1946, 75.00; current, from Jan. 1956,
subs. to regular ed., 25.00 per year; non-
subs., 100.00 per year   RDX   487

Congressional Record. 1957- to date 100.00 per year
RDX   488

The Conservator (Horace Traubel, ed.). Complete index
to Vols. 1-30 (March 1890-June 1919). Comp.
by H.S. Saunders. Toronto, 1920. 2.00 RDX   489

The Continent; an illus. weekly magazine, ed. by
Albion W. Tourgee. Vol. 1-6, no. 8 (Feb. 15,
1882-July 23, 1884). 69.00; single vols., 14.00
each   LoC   490

Corette, Michel--L'art de se perfectionner dans le
    violon. Paris [1783?] 1.50 UR   502

--------Methode, theorique et pratique. Pour apprendre
    en peu de tems le violoncelle ... Paris, 1741. 1.00
    UR   503

--------Le parfait maitre a chanter. Paris, 1782.
    1.50 UR   504

Cortambert, Louis Richard (P&R-2)--Voyage au pays de
    Osages. Un tour en Sicile. 5.95 LoC   505

Cotton stealing (S-B4). A novel. Chicago, J.R. Walsh
    & Co., 1866. ... 487p. 3.95 LoC   506

Cox & Atkinson (LR-E&W)--Registration. 1v. (1843-
    46). MMP   507

Cox, Macrae & Hertslet (LR-E&W)--County Court.
    3v. (1847-58). MMP   508

Cox, Sandford C. (OV-A5)--Recollections of the early
    settlement of the Wabash Valley. Lafayette (Ind.),
    Courier Steam Book & Job Printing House, 1860.
    160p. 3.75 LoC   509

Coyner, David H. (P&R-2)--The lost trappers ; a collec-
    tion of interesting scenes and events in the Rocky
    Mountains; ... 5.95 LoC   510

        Craddock, Charles Egbert (pseud.)--See Murfree,
        Mary Noailles

Crafford, John (TOS-1)--A new and most exact account
    of the fertile and famous colony of Carolina ... As
    also an account of the Islands of Bermudas, ...
    Dublin, printed for Nathan Tarrant ... 1683. 5.95
    LoC   511

Crakes, James G. (PH-64)--The anatomical, physiolog-
    ical and psychological differences between distance
    runners of varying abilities. 1960. Thesis (Ph.D.),
    Univ. of Oregon. 105p. 1.40   O   512

Creighton, Charles--A history of epidemics in Britain.
2v. 12.50 SM   513

Creswell (LR-E&W)--Bankruptcy. 1v. (1827-29). MMP514

Cresswell, Nicholas (TOS-4)--The journal of Nicholas
Cresswell, 1774-77. New York, L. MacVeagh, The
Dial Press, 1924. 5.95 LoC   515

Crevecoeur, Michel Guillaume St. Jean de (TOS-4)--
Letters from an American farmer; ... London,
printed for T. Davies ... & L. Davis, 1782. 5.95
LoC   516

Crim, Miss Matt (S-B3)--The Heathercotes. Savannah,
Ga., J.H Estill (c1880). 49p. 3.25 LoC   517

Cripp's Church & Clergy (LR-E&W)--Ecclesiastical.
1v. (1847-50). MMP   518

Croghan, George (TOS-1)--Journal of Col. George
Croghan, who was sent, after the Peace of 1763,
... to explore the country adjacent to the Ohio River,
... [Burlington, New Jer., New Jersey Enterprise
Book & Job Prtg. Establishment, 1875] 5.95 LoC   519

Croll, Oswald, 1580-1609 (HS-1)--Basilica chymica
...In fine libri additus est eiusdem autoris Tractatus
nouus de signatvris rervm internis. Coloniae Allo-
brogvm, Excudebat P. Marcellvs, 1610. 2v. in 1
8.50   LoC   520

Crosby, Alpheus, 1810 (AP-1)--The present position of
the seceded states, and the right and duties of the
general government in respect to them. An address to
the Phi Beta Kappa Society of Dartmouth College,
July 19, 1865. Boston, Press of G.C. Rand & Avery,
1865. 16p. 2.45 LoC   521

Crozier, Robert Haskins (S-B3)--Hal Gilman; or a
Mississippi story substantially true. Sardis, Miss.,
W.H. Crockett & Co., 1883. ...79p. 3.25 LoC   522

Cruz Brocarte, Antonio de la--Medula de la mvsica
theorica. Salamanca, 1707. 1.50 UR   523

Culbertson, Thaddeus A. (P&R-2)--Journal of an expedition to the Mauvaises Terres and the upper Missouri
in 1850. 5.95 LoC   524

Cuming, Fortescue (MFM, also TOS-2)--Sketches of a
tour to the western country, through the states of Ohio
and Kentucky; ... Pittsburgh, printed & pub. by
Cramer, Spear & Eichbaum, 1810. 5.95 LoC   525

Cumings, Samuel (TOS-4)--The Western pilot, containing charts of the Ohio river, and of the Mississippi ...
Cincinnati, Morgan, Lodge & Fisher, printers,
1825. 5.95 LoC   526

Cutler, Jervis (P&R-1, also OV-A4, TOS-1)--A topographical description of the State of Ohio, Indiana
Territory, and Louisiana. Comprehending the Ohio
and Mississippi rivers, and their principal tributary
streams: ... Boston, Pub. by Charles Williams,
J. Belcher, Printer, 1812. 5.95 LoC   527

Cutler, Russell (PSY-108)--Attitudes of male students
toward physical education in selected junior colleges
of California. 1958. Thesis (Ed.D.), Stanford Univ.
265p. 2.30   O   528

Cutts, James Madison (P&R-2)--The conquest of California and New Mexico, ... in the years 1846 & 1847.
5.95 LoC   529

Cuvier, Georges & Achille Valenciennes--Histoire naturelle
des poissons. Paris, Levrault, 1828-49. 22v.
57.00 F   530

                              D

Dabney, Robert Lewis (S-B4)--A defense of Virginia,
(and through her, of the South) in recent and pending
contests against the sectional party. New York, E.J.
Hale & Son, 1867. 356p. 3.95 LoC   531

--------(S-B4)--The new South. A discourse delivered
at the annual commencement of Hampden Sidney College, June 15th, 1892, ... Raleigh, N.C., Edwards,
Broughton & Co., printers. 1883, cover-title.
16p. 3.95 LoC   532

Dagron, M.--La poste par pigeons voyageurs. Souvenir
du siege de Paris. Tours-Bordeaux, 1870-71.
Nr. 361   (Nach dem Exemplar des Reichspostamts
Berlin). MK   533

Dana, Edmund (TOS-3)--Geographical sketches on the
western country; designed for emigrants and settlers:
... Cincinnati, Looker, Reynolds & Co., printers,
1819. 5.95 LoC   534

Dandridge, Mrs. Danske (Beddinger) (S-B4)--Rose
Brake; poems. New York, G.P. Putnam's Sons,
1890. vi, 110p. 3.95 LoC   535

Danson & Lloyd (LR-E&W)--Mercantile. 1v. (1828-
29)29). MMP   536

Darby, William (TOS-3)--The Emigrant's guide to the
western and southwestern states and territories ...
New York, Kirk & Mercein, 1818. 5.95 LoC   537

--------(TOS-4)--A geographical description of the state
of Louisiana. ... Printed for the author, and pub. by
John Melish, Philadelphia, ... 1816. 5.95 LoC   538

--------(TOS-2)--A new gazetteer of the United States
of America ... with the population of 1830. Hartford,
Hopkins, 1833. 5.95 LoC   539

--------(TOS-3)--View of the United States, historical,
geographical, and statistical; ... Philadelphia, H.S.
Tanner, 1828. 5.95 LoC   540

Darling, Fred E. (RC-29)--A leisure time analysis of
retired public school teachers in Kentucky. 1958.
Thesis (D.Rec.), Indiana Univ. 193p. 1.85 O   541

D'Arusmont, Frances Wright (TOS-1)--Views of society
and manners in America; ...during the years 1818-20.
By an Englishwoman. London, Longman, ... 1821.
5.95 LoC   542

50

Davies (LR-E&W)--Patent. 1v. (1785-1816). MMP   543

[Davis, Jefferson] (AP-1)--In memoriam. Jefferson
   Davis. A tribute of respect offered by the citizens
   of Charleston, S.C. Charleston, S.C., Walker,
   Evans, & Cogswell Co., 1890. 79p. 2.45 LoC   544

Davis, John (TOS-3)--Travels of four years and a half
   in the United States of America; during 1798, ...
   1802. ... London [etc. etc.]; New York, for R.
   Edwards, printer, 1803. 5.95 LoC   545

Davis, Katharine Norman (ACRL-103)--A check-list
   of Richmond, Virginia imprints from 1781 to 1805.
   1956. Thesis (M.S. in L.S.), Catholic Univ. of
   America. 1.50 UR   546

Davis, Mrs. Mary Evelyn (Moore) (S-B4)--Under the
   man-fig. Boston & New York, Houghton, Mifflin &
   Co., 1895. ... 323p. 3.95 LoC   547

--------(S-B4)--In war times at La Rose Blanche. 12
   illus. by E.W. Kemble. Boston, D. Lathrop Co.
   (c1888). ...257p. 3.95 LoC   548

--------(S-B4)--The wire cutters. Boston & New York,
   Houghton, Mifflin & Co., 1899. 373p. 3.95 LoC   549

Davis, William Watts Hart (P&R-1)--El Gringo; or,
   New Mexico and her people. 5.95 LoC   550

Davison & Merivale (LR-E&W)--King's Bench. 1v.
   (1843-44). MMP   551

Dawson, Simon James (P&R-1)--Report on the exploration
   of the country between Lake Superior and the Red
   River Settlement, and between the latter place and the
   Assiniboine and Saskatchewan. 5.95 LoC   552

Day, I. June (PE-386)--A study of the reduction of the
   waistline of women by maximum isometric contraction
   of the abdominal wall. 1957. Thesis (M.S.), Louisiana
   State Univ. 47p. 1.15 O   553

Day, Timothy C. (AP-1)--The Democratic Party as
it was and as it is! Washington, Buell & Blanchard,
printers, 1856. 7p. 2.45 LoC   554

Day's Election Cases (LR-E&W)--Election. 1v (1892-
93). MMP   555

Deacon (LR-E&W)--Bankruptcy. 4v. (1835-40). MMP   556

Deacon & Chitty (LR-E&W)--Bankruptcy. 4v. (1832-
35). MMP   557

Dearborn, Henry (TOS-2)--Revolutionary war journals
of Henry Dearborn, 1775-1783, ed. from the original
mss. by L. A. Brown and H. H. Peckham; with a biographical essay by H.D. Smith. Chicago, The Caxton
Club, 1939. 5.95 LoC   558

Debouchel, Victor (S-B3)--Histoire de la Louisiane
depuis les premieres decouvertes jus ou'en, 1840.
Nouvelle-Orleans, J.F. Lelievre, 1841. ...197p.
3.25 LoC   559

DeBow, J. --Industrial resources of the Southern and
Western states. 3v. 16.00 SM   560

De Colyar (LR-E&W)--County Court. 1v. (1867-82).
MMP   561

De Gex, Fisher & Jones (LR-E&W)--Bankruptcy. 1v.
(1860). MMP   562

De Gex, Jones & Smith (LR-E&W)--Bankruptcy.1v.
(1862-65). MMP   563

De Gex, Macnaghten & Gordon (LR-E&W)--Bankruptcy.
1v. (1851-57). MMP   564

De Gex & Jones' Appeals (LR-E&W)--Bankruptcy. 1v.
(1857-59). MMP   565

Degutis, Ernest William (PE-411)--Relationships between selected physical and motor factors and the pubes-
cent development of ten, thirteen, and sixteen year
old boys. 1960. Thesis (Ed.D.), Univ. of Oregon.
285p. 2.30 O   566

--------(PE-387)--Relationships between the standing
broad jump and various maturity, structural, and
strength measures of twelve year old boys. 1959.
Thesis (M.S.), Univ. or Oregon. 82p. 1.40   O   567

Delafield, John, 1812 (OV-A5)--An inquiry into the origin
of the antiquities of America. New York, Colt,
Burgess & Co. (etc., etc.), 1839. 142p. 3.55 LoC   568

De la Houssaye, Mme. S. (S-B3)--Pouponne et Balthazar,
nouvelle acadienne. Nouvelle-Orleans, Librarie de
l'Opinion, 1888. 217p. 3.25 LoC   569

Delane (LR-E&W)--Revision (Election). 1v. (1832-
35). MMP   570

Delano, Alonzo (P&R-1)--Life on the plains and among the
diggings, being scenes and adventures of an overland
journey to California: ... 5.95 LoC   571

De La Warr, Thomas West, 3rd lord (TOS-1)--The
relation of ... Lord De-La-Warre, ... London,
printed by Wm. Hall for Wm. Welbie, ... 1611.
5.95 LoC   572

De Leon, Thomas Cooper (S-B3)--Crag-nest. A romance
of the days of Sheridan's ride. Mobile, Ala., The
Gossip Prtg. Co., 1897. 220p. 3.25 LoC   573

--------(S-B4)--Joseph Wheeler, the man, the statesman,
the soldier, seen in semi-biographical sketches.
Atlanta, Ga., Byrd Prtg. Co., 1899. 142p. 3.95
LoC   574

--------(S-B4)--The pride of the Mercers. Philadelphia,
J.B. Lippincott Co., 1898. viii, 368p. 3.95 LoC   575

--------(S-B4)--The rending of the solid South; a consid-
eration ... Mobile, Ala., The Gossip Prtg. Co.,
1895. 32p. 3.95 LoC   576

--------(S-B4)--South songs; from the lays of later days.
Collected and ed., by T.C. DeLeon. New York,
Blelock & Co., 1866. ...153p. 3.95 LoC   577

DeLotto, Marcel Jacob (PSY-109)--The effects of
  competitive athletics on the growth and development
  of prepubescent boys. 1954. Thesis (Ph.D.), Univ.
  of Oregon. 175p. 1.90   O   578

Demers, Modeste (P&R-2)--Mission de Vancouver.
  Lettre de Monseigneur de Vancouver a un pretre de
  l'Archeveche. [Also included with Association de la
  Propagation de la Foi] 5.95   LoC   579

De Moss, John C. (KC-14)--A short history of the
  soldier-life, capture and death of William Francis
  Corbin, captain 4th Kentucky cavalry, C.S.A.
  (n.p., 1897). 32p. 3.95   LoC   580

Denny, Ebenezer (TOS-4)--Military journal ... With an
  introductory memoir [by W.H. Denny] Philadelphia,
  J.B. Lippincott & Co., for the Hist. Soc. of
  Pennsylvania, 1859. 5.95   LoC   581

Derby, James Cephas (S-B4)--Fifty years among authors,
  books and publishers. New York, G.W. Carleton
  & Co. (etc., etc.), 1884. ...739p. 3.95   LoC   582

Descourtilz, Miguel Esteban (TOS-3)--Voyages d'un
  Naturaliste, et ses observations faites sur les trois
  regnes de la nature, dans plusieurs ports de mer
  francois, en Espagne, au continent de l'Amerique
  septentrionale, ... Paris, Dufart, pere, 1809.
  3v. 5.95each. LoC   584

A detail of some particular services performed in America
  (TOS-2), during the years 1776-79. Comp. from journals
  and original papers, supposed to be chiefly taken
  from the journal kept on board the ship Rainbow, ...
  Printed for Ithiel Town, from a ms. obtained by him, ...
  New York, privately printed ..., 1835. 5.95   LoC   585

Devine, Barry Maxwell (PSY-110)--Analysis of responses
  on a sociometric questionnaire and the re-examination
  of structural and strength relationships for nine and
  eleven year old boys. 1960. Thesis (M.S.), Univ. of
  Oregon. 59p. 1.15 O   586

Devol, George H. (KC-12)--Forty years a gambler on the
   Mississippi. Cincinnati, Devol & Haines, 1887.
   300p. 4.79 LoC   587

Dickey, --William Alexander Percy: an alien spirit in
   the twentieth century. 2.10 KU   588

Dickinson, Jonathan (TOS-4)--Gods protecting providence,
   man's surest help and defence, ... Printed in Philadelphia
   by Reinier Jansen, 1699. 5.95 LoC   589

Dill, Richard (AP-1)--The American conflict: a lecture.
   Belfast, printed at the Daily "Northern whig" office,
   1863. 24p. 2.45 LoC   590

DiNucci, James Michael (PH-59)--Differences in metabolic levels between physically active and sedentary
   young men; optimal time of day for making such
   determination. 1957. Thesis (M.S.), Univ. of
   Illinois. 50p.   1.15 O   591

Dionigi, Marco--Primi tvoni, overo introdvzione del
   canto fermo ... Parma, 1667. 1.50 UR   592

Dioscorides, Pedianus, of Anazarbos (HS-1)--De medica
   materia libri sex. Parisiis, Apud S. Colinaeum,
   1537. 246 (i.e. 266)p. 4.42 LoC   593

Directory of the genealogical libraries and genealogical
   collections in the U.S. Reprinted from Bulletin No. 6
   (1938) of the American Genealogical Index. .80 GML 594

Dix, John A. (P&R-2)--United States of America. Report
   of the organization and proceedings of the Union Pacific
   Railroad Co. New York. 5.95 LoC   595

Dixon, -- Jesse Stuart and education. .70 KU   596

Dixon, Samuel Houston (S-B4)--The poets and poetry of
   Texas. Biographical sketches of the poets of Texas,
   with selections from their writings, containing
   review both personal and critical ... with an introd.
   by Wm. Carey Crane. Austin, Texas, S.H.Dixon &
   Co., 1885. 360p. 3.95   LoC   597

55

--------, 1855 (KC-12)--Robert Warren, the Texas
refugee. Thrilling story of field and camp life during
the late Civil War. New York, United States Book
Co., n.d. 568p. 7.74 LoC   598

Döhla, Johann Conrad (TOS-3)--Tagebuch eines Bayreuther soldaten, ... Mit einem vorwort von W.
frhr. v.Waldenfels. ... Bayreuth, Druck von L.
Ellwanger vorm. T.Burger, 1913. 5.95 LoC   599

Domenech, Emmanuel Henri Dieudonne (P&R-2)--
Seven years residence in the great deserts of North
America. 2v. 5.95 each LoC   600

Dörnberg, Karl Ludwig, freiherr von (TOS-3)--...
Tagebuchblätter eines hessischen offiziers aus der
zeit des nord-amerikanischen ... Pyritz, Backe'sche
buchdruckerei, 1899-1900. 5.95 LoC   601

Dorsey, Mrs. Sarah Anne (Ellis) (S-B4)--Panola. A
tale of Louisiana. Philadelphia, T.B. Peterson
& Brothers (c1877). ...261p. 3.95 LoC   602

Douglas (LR-E&W)--Election. 4v. (1774-76). MMP   603

Douglass, William (TOS-3)--A summary, historical and
political, ... of the British settlements in North
America; ... Boston, printed and sold by Rogers &
Fowle ... 1747-52. 2v. 5.95 each LoC   604

Dow, Lorenzo (TOS-3)--History of Cosmopolite; ...
experiences and travels, in Europe and America, ...
To which is added, the "Journey of Life," by
Peggy Dow. ... Cincinnati, published by Applegate
& Co., 1855. 5.95 LoC   605

Dow, Mrs. Peggy (TOS-4)--Vicissitudes exemplified; or,
The journey of life. ... New York, printed by J.C.
Totten, 1814. 5.95 LoC   606

Dowling & Lowndes (LR-E&W)--Bail Court. 7v. (1843-
49). MMP   607

Dowling & Ryland (LR-E&W)--King's Bench. 9v. (1822-
27). MMP   608

--------(LR-E&W)--Magistrates Cases. 4v. (1822-
27). MMP 609

Dowling's Practice Cases, New Series (LR-E&W)--
Bail. 2v. (1841-42). MMP 610

Dowling's Practice Cases (LR-E&W)--Bail. 9v. (1830
40). MMP 611

Downes, --A bio-bibliography of Norman Mailer. .70
KU 612

Dozier, Crion Theophilus (S-B3)--Foibles of fancy and
rhymes of the times. Birmingham, Ala., Dispatch
Prtg. Co., 1894. ... 218p. 3.25 LoC 613

Dragoon Expedition, 1839 (P&R-1)--Dragoon Expedition.
Fort Leavenworth, Oct. 3, 1839. Army & Navy
Chronicle, new series, vol. 9, 1839. 5.95 LoC 614

Drake, Daniel--Natural and statistical view, or picture
of Cincinnati and the Miami country. 2.75 SM 615

Drake, Daniel, 1785 (KC-13)--Pioneer life in Kentucky.
A series of reminiscential letters from Daniel Drake
... to his children. Ed. with notes and a biographical
sketch by his son, Charles D. Drake. Cincinnati,
R. Clarke & Co., 1870. 263p. 4.38 LoC 616

--------(KC-13)--A systematic treatise, historical,
etiological, and practical on the principal diseases of
the interior valley of North America, as they appear
in the Caucasian, African, Indian, and Esquimaux
varieties of its population. ... Ed. by S.H. Smith ...
and F.G. Smith. 2d ser. Philadelphia, Lippincott,
Grambo & Co., 1854. 985p. 12.33 LoC 617

Drake, Samuel Adams (P&R-1)--Hints and information
for the use of emigrants to Pike's Peak, ... 5.95 LoC 618

Drama of the Nineteenth Century. English and American
plays. Ed. by George Freedley. In units consisting
of approx. 5000 plays each. in prep RDX 619

Drayton, John (TOS-3)--A view of South-Carolina, as
respects her natural and civil concerns. Charleston,
printed by W. P. Young, 1802. 5.95 LoC   620

Drinkwater (LR-E&W)--Common pleas. 1v. (1840-41).
MMP   621

Driscoll, Eleanor A. (ACRL-99)--State legislative journals
for the period 1952-1953. 1956. Thesis (M.S. in
L.S.), Univ. of North Carolina. .75 UR   622

Duden, Gottfried (TOS-1)--Bericht über eine Reise nach
den westlichen Staaten Nordamerika's und einem
mehrjährigen Aufenthalt am Missouri (in den Jahren
1824-27), ... Elberfeld, Sam. Lucas, 1829. 5.95 LoC623

Dudley, William Wade, 1842 (AP-1)--The Iron Brigade at
Gettysburg. Official report of the part borne by the
1st brigade, 1st division, 1st army corps, ... in
action at Gettysburg, ... Cincinnati, priv. print.,
1879. ...15p. 2.45 LoC   624

Dugdale, Sir William--Monasticon Anglicanum. proposed,
20.00   F   625

Dugger, Shepherd Monroe (S-B3)--The balsam groves of
the Grandfather Mountains a tale of the western
North Carolina Mountains. Banner Elk, N.C. (Printed
by J.B. Lippincott Co., Philadelphia), 1892.
187p. 3.25 LoC   626

Dugué, Charles Oscar (S-B3)--Mila; ou, la more de La
Salle, drame en trois actes et en vers. Nouvelle-
Orleans, Impr. de J. L. Sollee, 1852. 43p. 3.25
LoC   627

DuLac, Francois Marie Perrin (P&R-2)--Voyage dans les
deux Louisianes, ... par les Etats-Unis, l'Ohio et les
provinces qui le bordent, en 1801-03; avec un apercu
des moeurs, ... des peuples de ces diverses contrees.
5.95 LoC   628

Dumas, Comte Mathieu (TOS-4)--Memoirs of his own
time; ... Philadelphia, Lea & Blanchard, 1839. 2v.
in 1 5.95 LoC   629

Dumas, William Thomas (S-B3)--The dinner horn.
Illus. & pub. by Paul T. Hill. Macon, Ga. (c1893).
3.25 LoC   630

Dunlavy, John (KC-9, KC-14)--The manifesto, or A
declaration of the doctrines and practice of the Church
of Christ. Pleasant Hill, Ky., P. Bertrand, printer,
1818. vi, 520p. 7.71 LoC   631

Dunbar, John (P&R-2)--Extracts from the journal of Mr.
Dunbar. 5.95 LoC   632

Dunkle, John J. (AP-1)--Prison life during the rebellion.
Being a brief narrative of the miseries and sufferings
of six hundred Confederate prisoners sent from Fort
Delaware to Morris' Island to be punished. Written
by Fritz Fuzzlebug (pseud.), one of their number. Pub.
by the author. Singer's Glen, Va., J. Funk's Sons,
printers, 1869. 48p. 2.45 LoC   633

Dunn, John (P&R-2)--History of the Oregon Territory and
British North-American fur trade ; with an account of
the habits and customs of the principal native tribes
on the Northern Continent. 5.95 LoC   634

Dunning (LR-E&W)--King's Bench. 1v. (1753-54).
MMP   635

Du Pratz, Antoine Simor Le Page (TOS-1)--Histoire de
la Louisiane, contenant la decouverte de ce vaste pays;
... Paris, De Bure, l'aine (etc.), 1758. 3v. 5.95
each LoC   636

Durand, of Dauphine (TOS-3)--Voyages d'un Francois,
exilé pour la religion, avec une description de la
Virginie & Marilan dans l'Amérique. La Haye,
Impr. pour l'autheur, 1687. 5.95 LoC   637

Du Roi, August Wilhelm (TOS-2)--Journal of DuRoi the
elder, ... Trans. from the original German ms.
... by C.S.J.Epping. [Philadelphia] Univ. of
Pennsylvania; New York, D. Appleton & Co., 1911.
5.95 LoC   638

Du Ru, Paul (TOS-1)--Journal ... (Feb. 1 to May 8, 1700) missionary priest to Louisiana; trans. with introd. and notes, from a ms. in the Newberry library, by R. L. Butler. Chicago, printed for the Caxton Club, 1934. 5.95 LoC 639

Duval, John Crittenden (S-B3)--The adventures of Big-foot Wallace, the Texas ranger and hunter. (Macon, Ga.), J.W. Burke & Co., 1870. 309p. 3.25 LoC 640

E

Eagle & Young (LR-E&W)--Tithe. 4v. (1204-1825). MMP 641

Earl Russell and the slave power (AP-1). Manchester, Union & Emancipation Soc., 1863. 11p. 2.45 LoC 642

Eastman, Mary H. (P&R-2)--The American annual; illustrative of the early history of North America. 5.95 LoC 643

The Economist (London). Vols. 1-50. proposed, 700.00 F 644

Editorial Research Reports (published four times a month, indexed semi-annually). Backfile, 1923-1956, 100.00; current, from Jan. 1957 - to subs. to regular ed., 8.00 per year; non-subs., 25.00 per year RDX 645

Edmundson, William (TOS-4)--A journal of life, travels, ... in the work of the ministry ... London, 1713. 5.95 LoC 646

Edwards, Frank S. (P&R-1)--A campaign in New Mexico with Colonel Doniphan. 5.95 LoC 647

Edwards, G. A. --Anglo-American foreign relations 1841-1861 with special reference to Trans-isthmian communication. Thesis (M.A.). 1.5. MMe 648

Edwards, Harry Stillwell (S-B4)--The Marbeau cousins.
Macon, Ga., J.W. Burke Co. (c1897). 294p. 3.95
LoC   649

--------(S-B4)--Two runaways, and other stories ...
with illus. by E.W. Kemble. New York, The
Century Co. (c1889). ... 246p. 3.95 LoC   650

Edwards, John Ellis, 1814 (KC-14)--Life of Rev.
John Wesley Childs; for twenty-three years an
itinerant Methodist minister. Richmond, Va. &
Louisville, Ky., J. Early for the Methodist Episcopal
Church, South, 1852. 295p. 3.95 LoC   651

Edwards, Philip Leget (P&R-1)--Rocky Mountain correspondence, from the Missouri Enquirer (Liberty).
5.95 LoC   652

Edwards, Samuel E. (OV-A5)--The Ohio hunter; or,
A brief sketch of the frontier life of Samuel E. Edwards,
the great bear and deer hunter of the State of Ohio.
Battle Creek, Mich., Review & Herald Steam Press
Print, 1826. 240p. 4.63 LoC   653

Eggleston, George Cary (S-B4)--A rebel's recollections.
New York, Hurd & Houghton ... 1874. vi, 260p.
3.95 LoC   654

Ehrenberger, M.B.H.--Novum et curiosum Laternae
magicae Augmentum. Math. Dissertation, Jena
1713. Nr.190 (Beschreibung einer Zauberlaterne
für bewegliche Bilder. Früher Vorgänger des
Kino). MK   655

Einstein, L.D.--The Italian Renaissance in England.
2.40 SM   656

Eisenbraun, Dalvin E. (PE-369)--A comparative analysis
of the Kraus-Weber test and the AAHPER test of physical fitness. 1958. Thesis (M.S.), South Dakota State
College. 82p. 1.25 O   657

Elder, William, 1806 (AP-1)--Debt and resources of the
    United States: and the effect of secession upon the trade
    and industry of the loyal states. Philadelphia,
    Ringwalt & Brown, 1863. 32p. 2.45 LoC   658

Elemjay, Louise (OV-A5)--Letters and miscellanies
    in prose, rhyme, and blank verse. Cincinnati,
    Moore, Anderson, Wilstach & Keys, 1852. 278p.
    5.05 LoC   659

Ellicott, Andrew (TOS-3)--Journal ... Philadelphia,
    printed by Budd & Bertram, for T. Dobson, 1803.
    5.95 LoC   660

Elliott, E.N., ed. (S-B4)--Cotton is king, and pro-
    slavery arguments: comprising the writings of
    Hammond, Harper, Christy, Stringfellow, Hodge,
    Bledsoe, and Cartwright on this important subject ...
    With an essay on slavery in the light of international
    law, by the editor. Augusta, Ga., Pritchard,
    Abbott & Loomis, 1860. ... 908p. 3.95 LoC   661

Elliott, Sarah Barnwell (S-B3)--A simple heart. New
    York, J. Ireland, 1887. 69p. 3.25 LoC   662

Elmore, James Buchanan (OV-A5)--A liver in Cuba, and
    poems. Alamo, Ind., The author, 1901. 188p.
    5.06; Supplement, Nashville, Tenn., McQuiddy
    Prtg. Co., 1902. 189-234p. 4.56 LoC   663

Ely, William (KC-10)--The Big Sandy Valley. A history
    of the people and the country from the earliest
    settlement to the present time. Catlettsburg,
    Ky., Central Methodist, 1887. 500p. 6.99 LoC   664

The Emigrant's guide (TOS-3), or pocket geography
    of the western states and territories, ... Cincinnati,
    pub. by Phillips & Speer, ... 1818. 5.95 LoC   665

Emmons, Richard (OV-A5)--The battle of Bunker Hill,
    or The temple of liberty; an historic poem in four
    cantos. New York, 1839. 144p. 3.57 LoC   666

--------(OV-A5)--The Fredoniad; or, Independence preserved. An epick poem on the late War of 1812. Boston, Pub. for the author, by W. Emmons, 1827. 4v. 2.50 each LoC 667

--------(OV-A5)--The national jubilee, and other miscellaneous poems. Washington, F.S. Meyer, printer 1830. 47p. 2.52 LoC 668

Emory, William Hemsley, et al. (P&R-1)--Notes of a military reconnoissance, from Fort Leavenworth, ... to San Diego, ... including parts of the Arkansas, Del Norte, and Gila Rivers. 5.95 LoC 669

English, William Hayden, 1822 (AP-1)--The Kansas question. Washington, D.C., printed at the Congressional Globe Office, 1858. 8p. 2.45 LoC 670

English neutrality (AP-1). Is the Alabama a British pirate? Philadelphia, B.Ashmead, 1863. 32p. 2.45 LoC 671

English plays--See Drama of the 19th century.

Entick, John (TOS-3)--The present state of the British empire. ... London, B. Law, 1774. 4v. 5.95 each LoC 672

Equity Reports (LR-E&W)--Equity. 3v. (1853-55). MMP 673

Erklärung der Representaten der vereinigten Colonien in Nord-Amerika ... nebst Kriegs-Reglement. Frankfurt und Leipzig, 1775. Nr. 209. MK 674

Errett, Isaac, ed., 1820 (KC-14)--Life and writings of George Edward Flower. Cincinnati, Standard Pub. Co., 1885. 338p. 3.95 LoC 675

Errington, Joseph (PE-370)--An evaluation of undergraduate professional preparation in physical education for men in Canada. 1957. Thesis (P.E.D.), Indiana Univ. 1v. 2.10 O 676

Escape of Gen. John H. Morgan & Capt. Thos. H. Hines
from the Ohio penitentiary, Nov. 27, 1863 (AP-1).
From ms. written Jan. 1864, by one of the Confederate officers confined in the penitentiary.
Franklin, Ky., Capital Print, n.d. Cover-title.
14p. 2.45 LoC   677

Espy, Josiah Murdoch (TOS-4, also KC-8)--Memorandums
of a tour ... in the states of Ohio and Kentucky and
Indiana territory in 1805. Cincinnati, R. Clarke
& Co., 1870. 5.95 LoC   678

Esquisse intéressant du Tableau fidele des causes qui
ont occasioné les revolutions actuelles de l'Amérique
Septentrionale (TOS-3), ... Revue & corrigé à Versailles.
Philadelphie, 1783. 5.95 LoC   679

Estcourt, J.H. (AP-1)--Rebellion and recognition.
Slavery, sovereignty, secession and recognition
considered. Manchester, Union & Emancipation
Soc., 1863. 28p. 2.45 LoC   680

Estes, Mary Margaret (PE-433)--The role of creative
play equipment in developing muscular fitness.
1959. Thesis (Ph.D.), State Univ. of Iowa. 84p.
1.40 O   681

Euler, Leonhard--Tentamen novae theoriae mvsicae ex
certissimis harmoniae principiis dilvcide expositae.
Petropoli, 1739. 3.75 UR   682

Evans (LR-E&W)--King's Bench (Lord Mansfield's Civil
Decisions). 2v. (1756-88). MMP   683

Evans, Estwick (MFM, also TOS-2)--A pedestrious tour
of four thousand miles through the western states and
territories, during ... 1818. Concord, N.H., printed
by Joseph C. Spear, 1819. 5.95 LoC   684

Everett--The imaginative fiction of J.R. Tolkien.
1.40 KU   685

Everett, Edward, 1794 (AP-1)--The great issues now
before the country. New York, G.Q. Colton, 1861.
Cover-title. 52p. 2.45 LoC   686

Ewell, John D. (TOS-3)--Life of Rev. William Keele,
　˳˳˳ Noah, Tenn., W.J. Stephenson, 1884. 5.95
LoC   687

Ewing, Thomas, 1789 (AP-1)--Letter to his excellency
Benj. Stanton, Lt. Gov. of Ohio, in answer to his
charges against our generals who fought in the
Battle of Shiloh, on the 6th of April, 1862.
Columbus, R. Nivins, printer, 1862. Cover-title.
24p. 2.45 LoC   688

Extrait du journal d'un officier de la marine de
l'escadre de M. le comte d'Estaing (TOS-2).
[n.p.] 1782. 5.95 LoC   689

Exum, William (PE-388)--The contributions of physical
education activities for the development of democratic
leadership abilities. 1957. Thesis (Ed.D.),
New York Univ. 261p. 2.30 O   690

Eyre, John (OV-A5)--Travels: comprising a journey
from England to Ohio, two years in that state,
travels in America, etc. To which are added the
foreigner's protracted journal, letters, etc. New
York, Sold at Riker's (etc.), 1851. 360p. 5.95
LoC   691

Eyre-Todd, George, ed. (BC-3)--Early Scottish
poetry: Thomas the Rhymer; John Barbour ; Androw
of Wyntoun: Henry the Minstrel. Glasgow, W.
Hodge, 1891. 220p. 4.41 LoC   692

--------(BC-3)--Medieval Scottish poetry. Glasgow,
W. Hodge, 1892. 269p. 4.95 LoC   693

--------(BC-3)--Scottish ballad poetry. Glasgow,
W. Hodge, 1893. 323p. 5.54 LoC   694

--------(BC-3)--Scottish poetry of the 16th century.
Glasgow, W. Hodge, 1892. 269p. 4.95 LoC   695

--------(BC-3)--Scottish poetry of the 17th century.
Glasgow, W. Hodge, 1895. 296p. 5.25 LoC   696

--------(BC-3)--Scottish poetry of the 18th century.
Glasgow, W. Hodge, 1896. 2v. v1, 5.61; v2 4.01 LoC 697

Fagan, William Long (S-B4)--Southern war songs.
Camp-fire, patriotic and sentimental, ... New York,
M.T. Richardson & Co., 1890. vi, 389p. 3.95 LoC 698

Fairbank, Calvin, 1816 (KC-14)--Rev. Calvin Fairbank
during slavery times. How he "fought the good fight,"
to prepare the "way." Ed. from his ms. Chicago,
Patriotic Pub. Co., 1890. xi, 207p. 3.95 LoC   699

Falconer, Thomas (P&R-1)--Expedition to Santa Fe. ...
5.95   LoC   700

Falconer & Fitzherbert (LR-E&W)--Election. 1v.
(1835-39). MMP   701

Fallacies of freemen and foes of liberty (AP-1). A
reply to "The American war: the whole question
explained." Manchester, Union and Emancipation
Soc., 1863. 36p. 2.45 LoC   702

Fanning, David (TOS-4)--The narrative of Col. David
Fanning, ... with an introd. [by J.H. Wheeler] and
explanatory notes. Richmond, Va., printed for private
distribution only, ... 1861. 5.95 LoC   703

Fardig, Elise B.   (ACRL-122)--The music collection
of the university library. 1958. Thesis (M.S.),
Florida State Univ. 1.50   UR   704

Farmer, Robert (TOS-1)--Letters from Illinois, extracts
from. In Clarence W. Alvord & Clarence C. Carter
(eds.), The new regime, 1765-1767, Illinois State
Hist. Library Collections, XI. ... 5.95   LoC   705

Farr, Edward, ed. (BC-3)--Select poetry, chiefly
sacred, of the reign of King James the First.
Cambridge, Univ. Pres, for J. & J.J. Deighton,
1847. 360p. 5.95 LoC   706

Farrow, Mildred Hayward (ACRL-120)--The history
of Guilford College Library, 1837-1955. 1959.
Thesis (M.S. in L.S.), Univ. of North Carolina.
2.25 UR   707

Faux, William (TOS-3)--Memorable days in America:
   being a journal of a tour to the United States, ...
   London, W. Simpkin & R. Marshall, 1823. 5.95
   LoC   708

Feltman, William (TOS-4)--The journal of Lieut. William
   Feltman, ... Philadelphia pub. for the Hist..Soc. of
   Pennsylvania, by H.C. Baird, 1853. 5.95 LoC   709

Fenning, David (TOS-2)--A new system of geography;
   or, a general description of the world. ... London,
   printed for S. Crowder, ... 1764-65. 2v. 5.95 each
   LoC   710

Fergusson, D. (P&R-2)--Letter of the Secretary of War,
   communicating, ... a copy of the report of Major D.
   Fergusson on the country, its resources, and the route
   between Tucson and Lobos Bay. March 14, 1863.
   5.95 LoC   711

Fernow, Berthold, 1837 (KC-13)--The Ohio valley in
   colonial days. Albany, N.Y., J. Munsell's Sons,
   1890. 299p. 4.78 LoC   712

Field, T.W.--An essay towards an Indian bibliography.
   2.50 SM   713

Fifth annual reunion of the 1st Kentucky Orphan Brigade,
   C.S.A. (AP-1), Cynthiana, Ky., Aug. 18, 1886.
   Frankfort, Ky., printed by the Western Argus,
   1887. 36p. 2.45 LoC   714

Figgis, J.M.--The political aspects of St. Augustine's
   City of God. 2.00 SM   715

Filson, John (TOS-3)--The discovery, settlement and present state of Kentucky; and an essay towards the
   topography and natural history ... Wilmington, Del.
   printed by James Adams, 1784. 5.95 LoC   716

Finley, James Bradley (OV-A5)--Autobiography...or,
   Pioneer life in the West. Ed. by W.P. Strickland, D.D.
   Cincinnati, Printed at the Methodist Book Concern for
   the author, 1853. 455p. 7.00 LoC   717

--------(OV-A5)--History of the Wyandott mission, at Upper Sandusky, Ohio, under the direction of the Methodist Episcopal Church. Cincinnati, Pub. by J.F. Wright & L. Swormstedt, for the Methodist Episcopal Church, 1840. 432p. 6.74 LoC   718

--------(MFM)--Life among the Indians. 1819. 548p. 7.52   LoC   719

Fish, C.--Civil Service and the patronage. 2.40 SM   720

Fisk, James Liberty (P&R-1)--Expedition to the Rocky Mountains. Letter from the Secretary of War in answer to a resolution of the House of Feb. 26, transmitting report of Capt. Fisk of his late expedition to the Rocky Mountains and Idaho. 5.95 LoC   721

Fitzgerald, Oscar Penn (S-B4)--California sketches. New and old. Nashville, Tenn., Publishing House of the M.E. Church, South, 1895. 336p. 3.95 LoC   722

--------(S-B4)--Judge Longstreet. A life sketch. Nashville, Tenn., Printed for the author [by the] Publishing House of the M.E. Church, South, 1891. 318p. 3.95 LoC   723

Flagg, Edmund, 1815-1890 (KC-14)--The far West; or, a tour beyond the mountains. Embracing outlines of western life and scenery: sketches of the prairies, river, ancient mounds, early settlements of the French, etc. New York, Harper & Brothers, 1838. 2v. 3.95   each LoC   724

Flint, James (Scotchman) (TOS-3)--Letters from America, ... Edinburgh, W. & C. Tait [etc.] 1822. 5.95 LoC   725

Flint, Thomas (TOS-2)--Recollections ... occasional residences and journeyings in the valley of the Mississippi, ... Boston, Cummings, Hilliard & Co., 1826. 5.95 LoC   727

Flint, Timothy (OV-A5)--Francis Berrian, or The Mexican patriot ... 2d ed. Philadelphia, Key & Biddle, 1834. 2v. v1, 4.98; v2, 3.50 LoC   728

--------(OV-A5)--The life and adventures of Arthur
Glenning ... (A novel). Philadelphia, Towar & Hogan,
1828. 2v. in 1 5.93 LoC   728

--------(OV-A5)--An oration, delivered at Leominster,
July 4, 1815, before the Washington benevolent soci-
eties of Lancaster and Sterling and Leominster and
Fitchburg. Worcester (Mass): Printed by William
Manning (1815). 24p. 2.50 LoC   729

Florez, Enrique--España Sagrada. proposed, 140.00
F   730

The Floure and the Leafe & The Boke of Cupide, God of
Love, or the Cuckow and the Nightingale. William
Morris, Kelmscott Press, London, 1896. Nr.102
(Typographische Kostbarkeit). MK   731

Flower, George (TOS-4)--...History of the English
settlement in Edwards county, Illinois, ... with preface
and footnotes by E.G. Washburne. ... Chicago,
Fergus Prtg. Co., 1882. 5.95 LoC   732

Flower, Richard (TOS-1)--Letters from Lexington and
the Illinois, ... London, J. Ridgway, 1819. 5.95
LoC   733

Folsom, George F. (P&R-1)--Mexico in 1842:...with a
sketch of its history, ... an account of Texas and
Yucatan; and of the Santa Fe expedition. Illus. with
a new map. 5.95 LoC   734

Folsom, Montgomery M. (S-B4)--Scraps of song and
Southern scenes ... a collection of humorous and
pathetic poems and descriptive sketches of plantation life in the backwoods of Georgia. Atlanta, Ga.,
C.P. Byrd, 1889. ...199p. 3.95 LoC   735

Fonblanque (LR-E&W)--Bankruptcy. 1v. (1849-52).
MMP   736

Fontaine, Jacques (TOS-4)--Memoirs of a Huguenot
Family. Trans. and comp. from the original auto-
biography of Rev. James Fontaine, and other family
mss., comprising an original journal of travels in
Virginia, New York, etc. in 1715 and 1716. By
Ann Maury. New York, G.P. Putnam, 1853. 5.95
LoC   737

Foote, Henry Stuart (S-B4)--An address, delivered before the Franklin Institute and Union Literary Societies
of Centenary College, Louisiana, July 27, 1852.
Jackson (La.), Printed at the office of the Southern
Star, 1852. 16p. 3.95 LoC   738

Forbes, James Grant (TOS-3)--Sketches, historical and
topographical, of the Floridas; ... New York, C.S.
Van Winkle, 1821. 5.95 LoC   739

Ford, Carol (PSY-93)--A comparison of the relative
effectiveness between two methods of teaching the whip
kick to college women enrolled in beginning swimming
classes. 1958. Thesis (Ed.M.), Woman's College,
Univ. of North Carolina. 50p. 1.15 O   740

Ford, G.S.--Stein and the Era of Reform in Prussia.
2.00 SM   741

Foreman, Carolyn (ACRL-118)--An analysis of publications issued by the American Library Association,
1907-57. 1959. Thesis (M.L.S.), Univ. of Texas.
2.25 UR   742

Forman, Benjamin Rice (AP-1)--The Confederate prisoners in northern prisons during the war. N.p.,
n.d. 19p. 2.45 LoC   743

Forman, Samuel S. (TOS-2)--Narrative of a journey down
the Ohio and Mississippi in 1789-90. With a memoir
and illustrative notes by L.C. Draper. Cincinnati,
Robert Clarke & Co., 1888. 5.95 LoC   744

Forrest, Michael (TOS-1)--Travels through America.
A poem. Philadelphia, printed by Johnston & Justice
... 1793. 5.95 LoC   745

Fort Kiowa Letter (P&R-2)--Letter from one of Ashley's
men, dated Fort Kiowa, June 17, 1823, ... Daily
National Intelligencer, Sept. 3, 1823. 5.95 LoC   746

Fortier, Alcee (S-B4)--Louisiana sketches. Literature,
customs and dialects, history and education. New
Orleans, F.F. Hansell & Bro. (1894). vi, 307p.
3.95 LoC   747

Forwood, William Stump, 1830 (KC-10)--An historical
and descriptive narrative of the Mammoth Cave of
Kentucky. Philadelphia, J.B. Lippincott & Co.,
1870. 225p. 3.97 LoC   748

Fox, Jesse W. (P&R-1)--General courses and distance
from G.S.L. City to Fort Limhi and gold diggings on
Salmon River. 5.95 LoC   749

Fox, John Willis (PE-371)--Practices and trends in
physical education programs for boys in selected
Oregon schools. 1958. Thesis (Ed.D.), Univ. of
Oregon. 537p. 3.15 O   750

Fox & Smith (LR-E&W)--Registration. 1v. (1886-95).
MMP   751

Franklin, John (P&R-2)--Narrative of a second expedition
to the shores of the Polar Sea, in the years 1825-27,
... Including the account ... by John Richardson, ...
5.95 LoC   752

Franklin, Jones (TOS-2)--The philosophical and pol-
itical history of the thirteen United States of America.
... London, J. Hinton & W. Adams, 1784. 5.95
LoC   753

Franklin, Joseph, 1834 (KC-14)--The life and times of
Benjamin Franklin, by Joseph Franklin and J.A.
Headington. St. Louis, J. Burns, 1879. xv, 508p.
3.95 LoC   754

Fraser (LR-E&W)--Election. 2v. (1790-92). MMP   755

Fraser, Alexander (TOS-1)--Report on the Illinois Country.
In Clarence W.Alvord & Clarence C. Carter (eds.),
The new regime, 1765-67, Illinois State Hist.
Library Collections, XI.5.95 LoC   756

Fredericksburg and Adjacent National Battlefields Memorial Park Assoc. (AP-1). ... Fredericksburg,
Va., The Free Lance,1899. Cover-title. ...27p.
2.45 LoC   757

Fremont, John Charles (P&R-2)--Geographical memoir
upon Upper California, in illustration of his map of
Oregon and California. 5.95 LoC   758

French, Benjamin Franklin, ed. (TOS-1)--Historical
collections of Louisiana, embracing translations of
many rare and valuable documents relating to the natural,
civil and political history of that state. Comp. with
historical and biographical notes, and an introd. ...
New York, Wiley & Putnam, 1846-1853. 5v. 5.95
each LoC   759

Freytas, Nicolas de (TOS-1)--The expedition of Don
Diego Dionisio de Peñalosa ... from Santa Fe to the
river Mischipi and Quivira in 1662, as described by
Father Nicolas de Freytas, O.S.F. ... Ed. by J.G.
Shea. New York, J.G. Shea, 1882. 5.95 LoC   760

Fries, E.--Hymenomycetes Europaei. 3.3.   MMe   761

Frobel, Julius (P&R-1)--Aus Amerika. Erfahrungen,
Reisen und Studien. 2v. 5.95 each LoC   762

Frost, John, 1800 (KC-14)--Life of Major General
Zachary Taylor; with notices of the war in New
Mexico, California, and in southern Mexico; and
biographical sketches of officers who have distin-
guished themselves in the war with Mexico. New York,
D. Appleton & Co. ... 1847. 346p. 3.95 LoC   763

Fry, James Barnet, 1827 (KC-14)--Operations of the
army under Buell from June 10th to October 30th,
1862, and the "Buell Commission." New York,
D. Van Nostrand, 1884. 201p. 3.95 LoC   764

Fuller, Thomas (BC-3)--The history of the worthies of
England. A new ed., containing brief notices of the
most celebrated worthies of England who have flourished
since the time of Fuller; with explanatory notes and
copious indexes. By P. Austin Nuttall. London,
T. Tegg, 1840. 3v. v1, 7.96; v2, 5.97; v3, 5.97
LoC   765

Furlong, Lawrence (TOS-1)--The American coast pilot;
... Newburyport, Blunt & March, 1796. 5.95 LoC   766

Fuzzlebug, Fritz (pseud.)--See Dunkle, John J.

                            G

Gaines, F.P.--The Southern plantation; study in the
development and accuracy of a tradition. 2.25 SM   760

Gale (LR-E&W)--Exchequer. 2v. (1835-36). MMP   761

Gale & Davidson (LR-E&W)--Queen's Bench. 3v.
(1841-43). MMP   762

Gall, Ludwig (TOS-2)--Meine Auswanderung nach den
Vereinigten-Staaten in Nord-Amerika im Frühjahr
1819 und meine Rückkehr nach der Heimath im Winter
1820. Frier, F.A. Gall, 1822. 2v. 5.95 each LoC 763

Galvin, Hoyt Rees--A program for a new public library
building for the Huntsville public library, Huntsville,
Alabama. .70 KU   764

--------A program for a new public library building
for the public library of Moultrie and Colquitt County,
Moultrie, Georgia. .70 KU   765

--------Waco public library report. .70 KU   766

Gano, John (TOS-2)--Biographical memoirs ...
written principally by himself. New York, Southwick
& Hardcastle for J. Tiebout, 1806. 5.95 LoC   767

Ganslen, Richard Victor (PH-60)--The influence of
training upon the aerobic and anaerobic metabolic
variables. 1953. Thesis (Ph.D.), Univ of Illinois.
115p. 1.40 O   768

Garfias, Robert A.--The basic melody of the Togaku
pieces of the Gagaku repertoire. 1958. Thesis
(M.A. in Mus.), Univ. of California (Los Angeles).
3.00 UR   769

Garland, H.--Crumbling idols. 2.00 SM   770

Garnett, Muscoe Russell Hunter, 1821 (AP-1)--The
Union, past and future; how it works, and how to
save it. By a citizen of Virginia. Charleston,
Steam-power Press of Walker & James, 1850. 55p.
2.45 LoC   771

Garrett, Pat F. (S-B4)--The authentic life of Billy,
the kid, the noted desperado of the Southwest, ...
Santa Fe, N. Mex., New Mexican Prtg. & Pub.
Co., 1882. 137p. 3.95 LoC   772

Garrett, Lewis (OV-A5)--Recollections of the West...
To which are added Fletcher's six letters on the spiritual manifestation of the Son of God. Nashville,
Printed at the Western Methodist Office, 1834.
240p. 4.63 LoC   773

Garrett, William (S-B4)--Reminiscences of public men
in Alabama, for thirty years. With an appendix.
Atlanta, Ga., Plantation Pub. Co.'s Press, 1872.
809p. 3.95 LoC   774

Garrettson, Freeborn (TOS-4)--The experience and
travels of ... Philadelphia, printed by Joseph
Crukshank ... 1791. 5.95 LoC   775

Gass, Patrick (P&R-1)--A journal of the voyages and
travels of a corps of discovery, under the command of
Capt. Lewis and Capt. Clarke ... through the interior
parts of North America to the Pacific Ocean, ...
5.95 LoC   776

Gebetbuch mit lateinischem und deutschem Text, Per-
gamenthandschrift. (15. Jahrhundert.) Stadtbibliothek Frankfurt am Main, Signatur: Ms. Germ.
Oct. 28 - Ausst. 41. Nr.178-179. MK   777

Genest, J. --Some account of the English stage from
the Restoration in 1660 to 1830. 10v. 30.00 SM   778

    Genet, Charles--See Memorial on the upward
    forces of fluids...

Genin, Thomas Hedges (OV-A5)--The Napolead; in twelve
books. St. Clairsville, O., Printed by H.J. Howard,
1833. 342p. 5.75 LoC   779

Gerdes, Glenn Richard (PSY-81)--The effects of various
motivational techniques upon performances in selected
physical tests. 1958. Thesis (Ph. D.), Indiana
Univ. 120p. 1.50 O   780

Gerstner, Clara (von Epplen-Hartenstein) von (KC-8)--
Beschreibung einer reise durch die Vereinigten Staaten
von Nord-Amerika in den jahren 1838 bis 1840. In
gesellschaft des ritters Franz Anton von Gerstner
unternommen. Leipzig, J.C. Hinrichs, 1842.
456p. 7.00 LoC   781

Geschichte und handlung der franzosischen pflanzstadte
in Norde-amerika (TOS-1), ... und den anspruchen der
erstern auf einen grossen theil von Canada und Louisiana.
Mit einer landcharte. Stutgart, J. Melzer, 1756.
5.95 LoC   782

Giles, Fleetwood (ACRL-113)--Texas librarians: a
study based on Who's Who in Library Service, third
edition, 1955. 1960. Thesis (M.L.S.), Univ. of
Texas. 2.25 UR   783

Gillespie, Dorwin Kenneth (HE-38)--The incidence and
prevalence of rheumatic fever in Lane County. 1959.
Thesis (Ph.D.), Univ. of Oregon. 107p. 1.25 O   784

Gillow, Joseph (BC-3)--A literary and biographical
history, or biographical dictionary, of the English
Catholics, from the breach with Rome in 1534, to
the present time. London, Burns & Oates, 1885-1902.
5v. v1, 7.38; v2, 3, 4, 5, 5.40 each LoC   785

Gilpin, Thomas (TOS-4)--Exiles in Virginia; ... Philadelphia, The subscribers, C. Sherman, printer,
1848. 5.95 LoC   786

Gilpin, William (P&R-1)--The central gold region. The
grain, pastoral, and gold regions of North America.
... 5.95 LoC   787

Girtch, Clarence Marvin (RC-35)--A survey of knowledge
and competencies of superintendents responsible for
combined park and recreation departments. 1957.
Thesis (M.S.), Univ. of Illinois. 98p. 1.40 O   788

Gist, Annie L. (HE-39)--Health misconceptions subscribed
to by freshmen in selected Negro colleges. 1955.
Thesis (Ed.D), New York Univ. 112p. 1.25 O   789

Gist, Christopher (TOS-4)--Journal ... 1753. Boston,
1836. 5.95 LoC   790

Glanville's Election Cases (LR-E&W)--Election. 1v.
(1623-24). MMP   791

Glass, Hugh (P&R-2)--Letters from the West. No. XIV.
The Missouri Trapper. 5.95 LoC   792

Glen, James (TOS-4)--A description of South Carolina;
... London, printed for R. & J. Dodsley, 1761.
5.95 LoC   793

Glines, Don (PSY-111)--Relationships of reaction,
movement, and completion times to certain motor,
strength, anthropometric and maturity measures.
1960. Thesis (Ph.D.), Univ. of Oregon. 126p.
1.65 O   794

Gloor, Reta Hollen (HE-40)--Misconceptions in social
hygiene among freshmen men and women at the
University of Oregon. 1958. Thesis (M.S.), Univ.
of Oregon. 55p. 1.05 O   795

Glover, Thomas (TOS-4)--An account of Virginia, its
scituation, temperature, productions, inhabitants, ...
Oxford, reprinted from the Philosophical transactions
of the Royal Society, June 20, 1676 [by H. Hart,
printer to the University] and sold by B.H. Blackwell,
1904. 5.95 LoC 796

Glyn & Jameson (LR-E&W)--Bankruptcy. 2v. (1821-
28). MMP 797

Gold Mines in Kansas - Rand & Avery, 1859 (P&R-2)--
A complete 1859 guide to the gold mines in Kansas and
Nebraska, with a description of the shortest and only
all railroad route to Kansas. ... 5.95 LoC 798

Goldsmith, J.? (TOS-4)--The present state of the
British empire in Europe, America, Africa and
Asia. ... London, W. Griffin, ... 1768. 5.95
LoC 799

Goode, William Henry (P&R-1)--Outposts of Zion,
with limnings of mission life. 5.95 LoC 800

Goodeve (LR-E&W)--Patent. 1v. (1776-1883). MMP 801

Gordon, Armistead Churchill (S-B3)--Befo' de war;
echoes in Negro dialect, by A.C. Gordon and Thomas
Nelson Page. New York, C. Scribner's Sons, 1888.
131p. 3.25 LoC 802

Gordon, John Brown, 1832 (AP-1)--The old south.
Addresses delivered before the Confederate Survivors'
Assoc. in Augusta, Ga., by J.B. Gordon and Charles
C. Jones, Jr. Augusta, Ga., Chronicle Pub. Co.,
1887. 23p. 2.45 LoC 803

Gott, John Kenneth (ACRL-102)--A check-list of Winchester, Virginia imprints from 1787 to 1876. 1953.
Thesis (M.S. in L.S.), Catholic Univ. of America.
1.50 UR 804

Gould, Emerson (MFM, also KC-11)--Fifty years on the
Mississippi, 1889. 9.73 LoC 805

Goulding, Francis Robert (S-B4)--The young marooners
on the Florida coast; or, Boert and Harold. New &
enl. ed. Philadelphia, J.S. Claxton, 1866. ...
446p. 3.95 LoC   806

Gow, Dan (AP-1)--Civil War in America; a lecture delivered in aid of the Lancashire relief fund, on Nov.
24, 1862. Manchester, Abel Heywood; London,
Simpkin, Marshall & Co., 1862. 34p. 2.45 LoC   807

Graham, Samuel (TOS-2)--Memoir ... Ed. by his son,
Col. J.J. Graham. Edinburgh, privately printed
by R. &R. Clark, 1862. 5.95 LoC   808

Grantham Sir Thomas (TOS-4)--An historical account of
some memorable actions, particularly in Virginia;
also against the admiral of Algier, and in the East
Indies: ... London, J. Roberts, 1716. 5.95 LoC   809

Graves, James Arnett--State aid in relation to library
legislation in the Southeastern states. 1.05 KU   810

Graves, John Temple (S-B4)--"The reign of the demagogue."
Delivered before the literary societies of the University
of Virginia, June 15th, 1893. Published by the Washington & Jefferson Societies. (Charlottesville) Charlottesville Chronicle Electric Print, 1893. 31p. 3.95
LoC   811

Gravier, Jacques (TOS-2)--Lettre du Père Jacques Gravier,
... le 23 Févriér 1708, sur les affaires de la
Louisiane. Nouvelle-York, De la presse Cramoisy
de Jean-Marie Shea, 1865. 5.95 LoC   812

--------(TOS-2)--Relation ou Journal du voyage du r.p.
Jacques Gravier, ... en 1700, depuis le pays de
Illinois jusqu'à l'embouchure du Mississippi. Nouvelle
York, Isle de Manate, De la presse Cramoisy de
Jean-Marie Shea, 1859. 5.95 LoC   813

Gray, John W. (TOS-2)--The life of Joseph Bishop, the
celebrated old pioneer in the first settlements of middle
Tennessee, ... Interspersed with racy anecdotes of
those early times. Nashville, Tenn., the author,
1858. 5.95 LoC   814

Grazer, Jean Hodges (RC-37)--Water safety instructional
material based on an analysis of drowning and present
practices in water safety instruction in Lake County,
Oregon. 1959. Thesis (M.S.), Univ. of Oregon.
82p. 1.40 O   815

Great Central Route - Majors & Byram (P&R-2)--The
Great Central Route via Nebraska City. 5.95 LoC   816

Greeley, Horace (P&R-1)--An overland journey from
New York to San Francisco, in the summer of 1859.
5.95 LoC   817

Green, Warren (KC-14)--A Blue-grass thoroughbred.
A novel by Tom Johnson (pseud.). Chicago, New York,
Belford, Clarke & Co. (etc. etc.), c1889. 216p.
3.95 LoC   818

Green, William (TOS-1)--The sufferings of William Green,
being a sorrowful account of his seven years transportation, ... London, J. Long [1774?] 5.95 LoC   819

Greenlee, Geraldine A. (PE-434)--The relationship of
selected measures of strength, balance and kinesthesis
to bowling performance. 1958. Thesis (M.A.), State
Univ. of Iowa. 48p. 1.15 O   820

Grenzeback, Jeanne Adeline (PSY-112)--Individual dif-
ferences in movement: a critical survey of research.
1958. Thesis (Ed.D.), Univ. of California. 190p.
1.90 O   821

Griffin (LR-E&W)--Patent. 1v. (1884-86); 1v. (1885-
87). MMP   822

Griffith (LR-E&W)--Poor Law. 1v. (1821-31). MMP   823

Griffith, John (TOS-2)--A journal of the life, travels,
and labours in the work of the ministry ... London,
James Phillips, 1779. 5.95 LoC   824

Griffith, Russell E., Jr. (PH-61)--The effect of the lack
of ascorbic acid on selected parasympathetic ganglia
cells in the guinea pig. 1958. Thesis (D. of Health
& Safety), Indiana Univ. 45p. 1.15 O   825

Gronovius, Joannes Fredericus (TOS-2)--Flora virginica,
exhibens plantas quas v.c. Johannes Clayton in
Virginia observavit atque collegit. ... Lugduni,
Batavorum, apud Cornelium Haak, 1739-1743.
5.95 LoC   826

Gross, Samuel David, 1805, ed. (KC-14)--Lives of
eminent American physicians and surgeons of the
19th century. Philadelphia, Lindsay & Balkiston,
1861. ... 836p. 3.95   LoC   827

Grund, Francis Joseph (OV-A5)--Aristocracy in America.
From the sketch-book of a German nobleman. Ed.
by Francis J. Grund. London, R. Bentley, 1839.
2v. in 1 4.93 LoC   828

Guest, Moses (OV-A5)--Poems on several occasions.
To which are annexed extracts from a journal, kept by
the author while he followed the sea, and during a
journey from New Brunswick, in New-Jersey, to
Montreal and Quebec. Cincinnati, Looker & Reynolds,
printers, 1823. 160p. 3.75   LoC   829

Gugl, Matthaeus--Fundamenta partiturae in compendio
data. Augspurg und Insprugg, 1757. 1.00 UR   830

Gunnison, John Williams & William Gilpin (P&R-1)--Guide
to the Kansas gold mines at Pike's Peak, ... 5.95
LoC   831

Guthrie, William (TOS-1)--A new geographical, historical, and commercial grammar, and present state of
the several kingdoms of the world ... London, J. Knox,
1770. 5.95 LoC   832

Guy's Hospital Reports. Vol. 106 (1957). 3.10 MMe   833

Gwillim's Tithe Cases (LR-E&W)--Tithe. 4v. (1224-
1824). MMP   834

Haag, Charles R. -- The keyboard concertos of Carl
Philipp Emanuel Bach. 1956. Thesis (Ph.D.),
Univ. of California (Los Angeles). 2.25 UR   835

Hager, Heinrich (?) (TOS-3)--Warhaffte Nachricht von
einer hochteutschen evangelischen colonie zu
Germantown, in nord-Virginien in America, ...
1720. In Historical notes relating to the Pennsylvania
Reformed church, ed. by Henry S. Dotterer, Vol.
I, no. 1 [1899] 5.95 LoC   836

Hahnemann, Samuel--Der Kaffee in seinen Wirkungen.
Leipzig, 1803 bei C.F. Steinacker. Nr.50. MK   837

Hale, John Peter (KC-8)--Daniel Boone. Some facts
and incidents not hitherto published. His ten or
twelve years' residence in Kanawha County. Wheeling,
L. Baker & Co., printers 188-. 18p. 2.50 LoC   838

Haliburton, T.C., ed. (MFM)--Traits of American
humor, by native authors. 1852. 3v. v1, 5.89;
v2, 5.39; v3, 5.39   LoC   839

Hall, David (ACRL-123)--The incidence and use of
phonograph records in a selected group of college
libraries. 1958. Thesis (M.S. in L.S.), Univ. of
North Carolina. 1.00 UR   840

Hall, Edward Hepple (P&R-1)--The Great West. Emigrants',
settlers' and travellers' guide and hand-book to the
States of California and Oregon, and the territories
of Nebraska, Utah, Colorado, Idaho, Montana, Nevada,
Washington, and Arizona. ... and a complete table of
distances. 5.95 LoC   841

--------(P&R-2)--Hall's guide to the Great West.
5.95   LoC   842

Hall, F. (TOS-1)--The importance of the British plantations in America to this kingdom; ... as also a description of the several colonies there. London, printed
for J. Peele, 1731. 5.95 LoC   843

Hall, Francis (TOS-2)--Travels in Canada, and in the
United States, in 1816-17. ... London, Longman,
... 1818. 5.95 LoC   844

Hall, Frederick (OV-A5)--Letters from the East and
from the West. Washington city, F. Taylor & W.M.
Morrison (etc. etc.); 1840. 168p. 3.84 LoC   845

Hall, James(TOS-4)--A brief history of the Mississippi
Territory, ... Salisbury, N.C., Francis Coupée,
1801. 5.95 LoC   846

--------(MFM)--Letters of the West. 1828. 385p.
5.73 LoC   847

--------(MFM)--Statistics of the West, at the close of
the year 1836. 284p. 4.61 LoC   848

--------(MFM, also OV-A2)--The West--its commerce
and navigation. 1848. 6.34 LoC   849

--------(P&R-1),also OV-A2)--The Wilderness and the
War Path. 5.95 LoC   850

Hall, Mary Frances (PSY-113)--A study of two methods
of teaching bowling to college women of high and low
motor ability. 1958. Thesis (Ph.D.), State Univ.
of Iowa. 54p. 1.15 O   851

Hall, Newman, 1816 (AP-1)--The American war.
London, J. Nisbet & Co. (etc.), 1862. 31p. 2.45
LoC   852

--------(AP-1)--The pro-slavery religion of the south.
Manchester, Union & Emancipation Soc., 1863. 2p.
2.45 LoC   853

Hamilton, Henry (TOS-1)--The Report by Lt.-Gov. Henry
Hamilton on His Proceedings from Nov. 1776 to
June, 1781. In Michigan pioneer and historical
collections, 1874-1929, IX ... 5.95 LoC   854

Hammond, John (TOS-1)--Hammond versus Heamans.
Or, An answer to an audacious Pamphlet, published
by ... Roger Heamans,... Printed at London for the
use of the author, and are to be sold at the Royall
Exchange in Cornhill, 1655. 5.95 LoC   855

Hamor, Ralph, the younger (TOS-4)--A trve discovrse of
the present estate of Virginia, and the successe of
affaires there till the 18 of Iune, 1614. ... London,
printed by Iohn Beale for W. Welby, 1615. 5.95 LoC 856

Hanley, Miles L.--Index to rimes in American and English
poetry, 1500-1900. Madison, Wis., The Microcard
Foundation, 1959. 600.00 F   857

Harben, William Nathaniel (S-B3)--White Marie; a story
of Georgian plantation life. New York, Cassell & Co.
(c1889). 250p. 3.25 LoC   858

Harding, Benjamin (KC-8)--A tour through the Western
country, A.D. 1818 & 1819. New London, Printed by
Samuel Green, for the author, 1819. 17p. 2.50
LoC   859

Hare, Joseph Thompson (TOS-1)--Life and dying confession
of Joseph T. Hare, the noted robber who was executed
... for robbing the mail. Auburn [N.Y.] printed by
D. Rumsey, 1818. 5.95 LoC   860

Harkness, William Winfred (PE-435)--The contributions
of A.F.R.O.T.C. and physical education experiences
to selected components of fitness of college men.
1957. Thesis (Ph.D.), Stanford Univ. 138p. 1.65 O 861

Harmon, Daniel Williams (P&R-1)--A journal of voyages
and travels in the interior of North America, ...
Illus. by a map of the country. 5.95 LoC   862

Harriott, John (TOS-3)--Struggles through life, exemplified in various travels and adventures ... London,
printed (for the author) by C. & W. Galabin, ...
1807. 2v. 5.95 each LoC   863

Harris, Dorothy Virginia (PE-372)--A comparison of
physical performance and psychological traits of college
women with high and low fitness indices. 1957. Thesis
(M.Ed.), Woman's College, Univ. of North Carolina.
81p. 1.25 O   864

Harris, Marcille Hurst (HE-49)--Parent-teacher attitude
toward sex education and the film, Human Growth.
1949. Thesis (M.S.), Univ. of Oregon. 55p.
1.15 O   865

Harris, Thaddeus Mason (TOS-3)--The Journal of a tour
into the territory northwest of the Alleghany mountains;
... Boston, Manning & Loring, 1805. 5.95 LoC   866

Harris, William Tell (TOS-1)--Remarks made during a
tour through the United States of America, in the
years 1817-19. ... London, Sherwood, Neely, & Jones,
1821. 5.95 LoC   867

Harrison, James C.E. (PE-373)--The relationships
between selected physical and motor factors and the
skeletal maturity of nine, twelve, and fifteen year
old boys. 1959. Thesis (Ph.D.), Univ. of Oregon.
187p. 1.75 O   868

Harrison, Samuel Alexander (TOS-2)--Memoir of Lieut.
Col. Tench Tilghman, ... [By Oswald Tilghman]
Albany, J. Munsell, 1876. 5.95 LoC   869

Harrison & Rutherford (LR-E&W)--Common pleas.
1v. (1865-66). MMP   870

Harrison & Wollaston (LR-E&W)--Common pleas.
2v. (1835-36). MMP   871

Hart, Thomas A. (PSY-114)--The establishment of principles of human relations that may be used in the
transition of all-white or all-Negro camps to inter-
racial camps. 1958. Thesis (Ed.D.), New York Univ.
257p. 2.30   O   872

Hart, Thomas George (PE-436)--A study of backgrounds
and present characteristics of male college freshmen
with low motor ability. 1959. Thesis (M.Ed.),
Pennsylvania State Univ. 60p. 1.15 O   873

Hartridge, Walter Charlton (TOS-4)--The letters of Robert
Mackay ... written from ports in America and England,
1795-1816. Athens, Ga., Univ. of Georgia Press,
1949. 5.95 LoC   874

Hartwell, Henry (TOS-4)--The present state of Virginia, and the college; ... London, printed for J. Wyat, 1727. 5.95 LoC 875

Haslewood, Joseph, ed. (BC-3)--Ancient critical essays upon English poets and poesy. London, Printed by Harding & Wright for Robert Triphook, 1811-15 2v. v1, 5.96; v2, 3.97 LoC 876

Haslop, G.S.B.--Anglo-native relations in early Stuart times up to 1644. Thesis (M.A.). 0.10.6 MMe 877

Hatch--The Ascham letters. 7.70 KU 878

Hawks, Francis Lister (KC-12)--The adventures of Daniel Boone, the Kentucky rifleman. ... New York, D. Appleton & Co. (etc.), 1850. 174p. 3.40 LoC 879

Hawley, Zerah (OV-A5)--A journal of a tour through Connecticut, Massachusetts, New-York, the north part of Pennsylvania and Ohio, including a year's residence in that part of the State of Ohio, styled New Connecticut, or Western Reserve. New- Haven, Printed by S. Converse, 1822. 158p. 3.73 LoC 880

Hayden, Ferdinand Vandiveer (P&R-1)--Contributions to the ethnography and philology of the Indian tribes of the Missouri Valley. 5.95 LoC 881

Hayden, Ferdinand Vandiveer & Joseph Leidy (P&R-2)-- Geological sketch of the estuary and fresh water deposit forming the bad lands of the Judith River, ... 5.95 LoC 882

Hayman, Noel R. (PSY-82)--Reduction of the number of bone assessments necessary for skeletal age determination of adolescent boys. 1959. Thesis (Ph.D.), Univ. of Oregon. 103p. 1.25 O 883

Hazlitt, William Carew (BC-3)--Prefaces, dedications, epistles selected from early English books, 1540- 1701. London, 1874. 447p. 6.91 LoC 884

--------, comp. (BC-3)--Remains of the early popular poetry of England. London, J.R. Smith, 1864-66. 4v. v1, 5.72; v2, 3, 4 3.75 each LoC 885

Hearndon Fam.--Ancestors and descendants of John
   Hearndon of Scituate, R.I. By Ruth S.D. Eddy. With
   typed index. Providence, R.I., 1944. 77p.
   1.75 GML   886

Heck, Johann Caspar--A complete system of harmony.
   London [1768] 1.00 UR   887

Hecke, J. Valentin (TOS-2)--Reise durch die Vereinigten
   Staaten von Nord-Amerika in den Jahren 1818-19. ...
   Berlin, In commission bei H.P. Petri, 1820-21.
   2v. 5.95 each LoC   888

Hedden, Gerald Wayne (HE-50)--Health needs of 1620
   freshmen in three high schools of Kern County Union
   High School and Junior College District. 1955. Thesis
   (Ed.D), Stanford Univ. 220p. 2.05 O   889

Heinsohn--Cason's "La Dama del Alba." 1.40 KU   890

Heisel, William A. (PSY-83)--An investigation into human
   head balance. 1958. Thesis (M.S.), Univ. of Michigan.
   31p. 1.05 O   891

   Henderson, J. Stanley (pseud.)--See Willett, Edward

Hennepin, Louis (TOS-4)--Description de la Louisiane,
   nouvellement decouverté au sud-oüest de la Nouvelle
   France, ... Paris, Chez la veuve Sebastien Hure,
   1683. 5.95   LoC   892

Henry, Alexander (P&R-1)--Travels and adventures in
   Canada and the Indian territories, between the years
   1760 and 1766. 5.95 LoC   893

Herne, Peregrine, pseud. (P&R-1)--Perils and pleasures
   of a hunter's life; or the romance of hunting. 5.95
   LoC   894

Herrington, W.D. (S-B3)--The deserter's daughter.
   Raleigh, W.B. Smith & Co., 1865. 27p. 3.25 LoC   895

Herrold, Zadia Cary (PE-389)--A comparison of methods
   for augmenting strength through progressive resistance
   exercise. 1956. Thesis (P.E.D.), Indiana Univ.
   89p. 1.40 O   896

Hertz, Gilman W. (PSY-94)--The effectiveness of three
methods of instruction in one-hand foul shooting.
1956. Thesis (P.E.D.), Indiana Univ. 116p. 1.40 O 897

Hess, Ford Allen (PE-437)--American objectives of
physical education from 1900-1957 assessed in the light
of certain historical events. 1959. Thesis (Ed.D.),
New York Univ. 459p. 3.00 O   898

Hesse, Johann Heinrich--Kurze, doch hinlangliche
anweisung zum general-basse. Hamburg [1776]
1.00 UR   899

Hewatt, Alexander (TOS-1)--An historical account of the
rise and progress of the colonies of South Carolina
and Georgia. ... London, printed for A. Donaldson,
1779. 2v. 5.95 each LoC   900

Hewett, Daniel (TOS-2)--The American traveller; or,
National directory, containing an account of all the
great post roads, ... Washington, printed by Davis
& Force, 1825. 5.95 LoC   901

Hibernicus; or Memoirs of an Irishman, now American:
(OV-A5) containing an account of the principal events
of his life, both before and since his emigration; ...
Pittsburgh, printed for the author by Cramer &
Spears, 1828. 251p. 4.75 LoC   902

Hicks, J.D.--The Populist revolt, a history of the
Farmers' Alliance and the People's Party. 2.75 SM   903

Hildeburn, C.S.--A century of printing--the issues of the
press in Pennsylvania 1685-1784. 2v. 8.00 SM   904

Hildreth, James (P&R-1, also OV-A4)--Dragoon
campaigns to the Rocky mountains; ... together
with incidents of a soldier's life, ... 5.95 LoC   905

Hill, Daniel Harvey, 1859 (AP-1)--The old south. An
address...on Memorial Day, June 6, 1887, before the
Society of the Army and Navy of the Confederate States
in the State of Maryland. Baltimore, Andrew J.
Conlon, 1887. 23p. 2.45 LoC   906

Hill, J. Douglas & Ladd, Richard S.--Treasure maps
in the Library of Congress. Rev. ed. Library of
Congress, Reference Dept., Map Division, Washington,
D.C., 1957. LC   907

Hillar, Paul Michael (PE-374)--Nutritional supplementa-
tion and motor performance of elementary school
children. 1955. Thesis (Ed.D.), Stanford Univ.
78p. 1.25 O   908

Hilton, William (TOS-1)--A relation of a discovery
lately made on the coast of Florida, ... Together with
proposals ... to all ... first settlers ... London,
Printed by J.C. for S. Miller, 1664. 5.95 LoC   909

Hind, Henry Youle (P&R-2)--British North America.
Reports of progress, together with a preliminary and
general report, on the Assiniboine and Saskatchewan
exploring expedition; ... 5.95 LoC   910

--------(P&R-1)--Narrative of the Canadian Red River
exploring expedition of 1857 and of the Assiniboine
and Saskatchewan exploring expedition of 1858. 2v.
5.95 each LoC   911

--------(P&R-2)--North-West Territory. Reports of
progress; together with a preliminary and general
report on the Assiniboine and Saskatchewan exploring
expedition, ... 5.95 LoC   912

--------(P&R-2)--Report on a topographical and geological exploration of the canoe route between Fort William,
Lake Superior, and Fort Garry, Red River; ... during
the summer of 1857. ... 5.95 LoC   913

Hisey, Carol Nan (PSY-84)--A comparison of selected
physical performance and emotional characteristics
of two groups of former high school athletes in girls'
basketball. 1957. Thesis (M.Ed.), Woman's College,
Univ. of North Carolina. 60p. 1.05 O   914

Hispanic American Historical Review. Vols. 1-22.
in prep C   915

The history of North America (TOS-3). Containing an
exact account of their first settlements; ... With the
present state of the different colonies; ... London,
sold by Millar [etc.] 1776. 5.95 LoC   916

History of Science. Group 1 (...famous books in the
European scientific tradition. .... a selection of
outstanding works in experimental medicine, chemistry,
and pharmacology. ...). Group price, 4.95 per
vol. LoC   917
The titles in this series are:

   Avicenna--Libri in re medica ...
   Bock, H.--Hieronymi Tragi, De stirpivm, maxime
      earvm, ...
   Brunschwig, H.--Thesavrvs pavpervm; ...
   Choulant--Graph. Incun., ...
   Cordus, V. --Dispensatorivm; ...
   Croll, O.--Basilica chymica ...
   Dioscorides, P., of Anazarbos--De medica materia
      libri sex.
   Hortus sanitatis [Maior]--ORtus SAnitatis.
   Jenner, E.--Inquiry into the causes and effects
      of the Variolae Vaccinae.
   Lemery, N.--Cours de chymie.
   Mesuê, J.--Mesue cum expositione mondini ...
   Mesuê, J. --Opus qbuslibet aromatariis: ...
   Monardes, N.--Primera y segvnda y tercera
      partes de la historia medicinal ...
   Mynsicht, A.--Thesavrvs et armamentarivm
      medico-chymicvm.
   Paracelsus--Archidoxa Philippi Theophrasti
      Paracelsi Bombast...
   El ricettario dell 'arte, et vniversita de medici, ...
   Saladino da Ascoli, 15th cent.--...Serenitati
      principis Tarenti phisici principalis ...
   Schoepf, J.D.--Materia medica Americana ...
   Scribonius Largus--De compositione medicamentoru
      liber, ...
   Turner, W.--A new herball.

History of the Ohio falls cities and their counties, with
   illustrations and biographical sketches (KC-13).
   Cleveland, O., L.A. Williams & Co., 1882. 2v.
   v1, 6.49; v2, 5.01 LoC   918

Hockersmith, Lorenzo Dow, 1833 (KC-14)--Morgan's
    escape. ... A true story of the raid of General Morgan
    and his men through Kentucky, Indiana and Ohio.
    Madisonville, Ky., Glenn's Graphic Print, 1903.
    ...54p. 3.95   LoC   919

Hodge, George Baird, 1828 (AP-1)--Sketch of the
    1st Kentucky Brigade, by its Adj. Gen., G.B.
    Hodge. Frankfort, Ky., printed at the Kentucky
    Yeoman Office, Major & Johnston, 1874. 31p. 2.45
    LoC   920

Hodges (LR-E&W)--Common pleas. 3v. (1835-37).
    MMP   921

Hodges Gen.--Genealogical record of the Hodges family
    in New England from 1633 to 1853. By Almon D.
    Hodges. Boston, 1853. 71p. 1.10 GML   922

Hodgson, Adam (TOS-3)--Letters from North America,
    written during a tour in the United States and Canada.
    ... London, Hurst, Robinson & Co., 1824. 2v.
    5.95 each LoC   923

--------(TOS-3)--Remarks during a journey through
    North America in the years 1819-21, ... Collected,
    arranged and published by Samuel Whiting. New
    York [J.Seymour, printer] 1823. 5.95 LoC   924

Hofmann, James A. (PE-412)--A comparison of the
    effect of two programs of weight training on explosive
    force. 1959. Thesis (M.S.), South Dakota State
    College. 69p. 1.15   O   925

Holcombe, Henry (TOS-2)--The First Fruits in a series
    of letters. Philadelphia, printed for the author by
    Ann Cochran, 1812. 5.95 LoC   926

Holdredge, Sterling M. (P&R-2)--State, territorial and
    ocean guide book of the Pacific: containing the time
    and distance tables, ... Also rates of postage to all
    parts of the world; ... To which is added nine large
    and accurate maps, ... 5.95   LoC   927

Holladay, Benjamin (P&R-1)--Table of distances of the
Overland Daily Stage Line from Atchison, Kansas,
to Great Salt Lake City, ... 5.95 LoC   928

Holley, Horace (KC-9)--A discourse occasioned by the
death of Col. James Morrison, delivered in the Episcopal Church, Lexington, Ky., May 19th, 1823.
Lexington, printed by J. Bradford, 1823. 37p. 2.50
LoC   929

Holme, Benjamin (TOS-4)--A collection of the epistles
and works of Benjamin Holme. To which is prefix'd,
an account of his life and travels ... London, Luke
Hinde, 1753. 5.95 LoC   930

Holmes, Isaac (TOS-3)--An account of the United States
of America, derived from actual observations, during
a residence of four years ... London, printed at the
Caxton Press, ... [1823] 5.95 LoC   931

Holmes, Reuben (P&R-2)--Sketch of the life of
"Chee-ho-Carte;" or, The Five Scalps. By "Oakly."
5.95 LoC   932

Holt, Joseph, 1807 (AP-1)--Speech of Hon. Joseph Holt,
of Kentucky, at Irving Hall, New York, Sept. 3, 1861.
New York, G.P. Putnam, 1861. 8p. 2.45 LoC   933

Holt's Admiralty Cases (LR-E&W)--Admiralty. 1v.
(1863-67). MMP   934

Holt's Judgments in Ashby v. White and Re Patey et al.
(LR-E&W)--King's Bench. 1v. (1702-05). MMP   935

Hood, John Bell (AP-1)--History of Gen. John Bell
Hood. New York, Knapp & Co., 1888. 15p. 2.45
LoC   936

Hoover, Francis Lentz (PE-375)--A history of the National
Association of Intercollegiate Athletics. 1958.
Thesis (P.E.D.), Indiana Univ. 265p. 2.10 O   937

"Hoover Commission" Task Force Report on Legal
Services and Procedure. Part IV, appendices and
charts. Feb., 1955. 3.00 AB   938

Hope, James Barron (S-B3)--Arms and the man: a
metrical address recited on the one hundredth anniversary (October 19th, 1881) of the surrender of Lord
Cornwallis at Yorktown, on invitation of Joint Committee
of both houses of Congress. Norfolk, Va.,
Landmark Pub. Co., 1882. 104p. 3.25 LoC   939

Hope, James Barron (S-B3)--A collection of poems.
Richmond, Va., A. Morris, 1850. 139p. 3.25
LoC   940

--------(S-B3)--An elegiac ode; recited by J.B. Hope,
on the occasion of completing the monument erected
by the ladies of Warren County, N.C., over the remains of Annie Carter Lee. Richmond, Examiner
Job Print, 1866. 29p. 3.25 LoC   941

--------(S-B3)--A poem: pronounced by J.B. Hope,
on the 250th anniversary of the English settlement
at Jamestown, May 13th, 1857. Richmond, C.H.
Wynne, Printer, 1857. 16p. 3.25 LoC   942

--------(S-B4)--Under the empire; or, The story of
Madelon. Norfolk, Va., J.B. Hope & Co., 1878.
211p. 3.95 LoC   943

--------(S-B3)--A wreath of Virginia bay leaves.
Poems by J.B. Hope. Selected and ed. by his daughter,
Janey Hope Marr. Richmond, Va., West, Johnston
& Co., 1895. 15-159p. 3.25 LoC   944

Hopwood & Coltman (LR-E&W)--Registration. 2v.
(1868-78). MMP   945

Hopwood & Philbrick (LR-E&W)--Registration. 1v.
(1863-67). MMP   946

Horn & Hurlstone (LR-E&W)--Exchequer. 2v.
(1838-39). MMP   947

Horner, William B. (P&R-2)--Horner's Kansas and
Nebraska gold regions, and new railroad and route
map, ... 5.95 LoC   948

Horton, Doris Ann (RC-43)--An analysis of selected
factors in influencing the choice of leisure time
activities of senior citizens in Conway, Arkansas.
1959. Thesis (M.A.), State Univ. of Iowa. 110p.
1.40   O   949

Hortus sanitatis [maior] (HS-1)--ORtus SAnitatis.
[Strassburg, J. Prüss, ca.1499-1503] 360p.
illus. 5.40   LoC   950

Hoskins, James (TOS-3)--Narrative of a voyage from
England, to the United States of North America; with
travels through part of eight of the states; ᵒᵒᵒ
Penzance, Eng., Printed for the author, by T. Vigurs,
1813. 5.95   LoC   951

Hovey, Horace Carter, 1833 (KC-11)--Mammoth Cave
of Kentucky; an illustrated manual, by H.C. Hovey
and Richard Ellsworth Call. Louisville, J.P. Morton
& Co., 1899. 111p. 2.71   LoC   952

Howard Gen.--A history of Isaac Howard of Foster,
R.I., and his descendants. By Daniel Howard. With
typed index. Windsor Locks, Conn., 1901. 56p.
2.00   GML   953

Howe, Henry (MFM)--The Great West. Enl. ed.,
1857. 2v. in 1 12.59   LoC   954

--------(MFM)--Historical collections of Ohio. 1847.
581p. 7.88   LoC   955

--------(KC-14)--The times of the rebellion in the
West: a collection of miscellanies, showing the part
taken in the war by each western state. Cincinnati,
Howe's Subscription Book Concern, 1867. 252p.
3.95   LoC   956

Howlin, James Roy (PE-413)--Comparing physical fitness in selected areas in Sioux Falls, South Dakota
with the national norms and Laporte score card.
1959. Thesis (M.S.), South Dakota State College.
86p. 1.40   O   957

Hoxie Fam.--The Hoxie family. Three centuries in
America. By Leslie R. Hoxie. With typed index.
Ukiah, Ore., 1950. 296p. 2.50 GML   958

Hubner, Charles William (S-B4)--Poems and essays.
New York, Brown & Derby, 1811. 172p. 3.95 LoC   959

---------(S-B4)--Wild flowers. Poems. New York,
The Author's Pub. Co., 1877. ...183p. 3.95 LoC   960

Hughes, A. M.--Short term adult residential college
problems of post-war Britain. Thesis (B.A.). 1.1
MMe   961

Hughes, John Taylor (P&R-2)--Doniphan's expedition;
containing an account of the conquest of New Mexico;
... with a sketch of the life of Col. Doniphan.
Illus. 5.95 LoC   962

Hughes, June Phillips (ACRL-116)--The Brazilian Institute
of Bibliography and Documentation...its history, organization and functions. 1959. Thesis (M.S. in L.S.),
Western Reserve Univ. 1.00 UR   963

Hughes, Thomas, 1822 (AP-1)--The cause of freedom:
which is its champion in America, the North or the
South? London, The Emancipation Soc., 1863. 16p.
2.45 LoC   964

Hull, Mary Frances (PE-376)--A critical view of the men
and women athletes of the years, 1931-1956. 1957.
Thesis (M.A.), Ohio State Univ. 106p. 1.25 O   965

Hull, Thomas V.--The origin and development of the
Indianapolis Public Library, 1873-1899. 1956.
Thesis (M.A.), Univ. of Kentucky. 1.05 KU   966

Hulme, Thomas (TOS-1)--...Journal, made during a
tour in the Western countries of America, ... In
Wm. Cobbett, A year's residence in the United
States of America ... Pt. 3, pp. 439-519. 2d ed.
5.95   LoC   967

--------(TOS-1)--Journal. In A year's residence in the
United States, by Wm. Cobbett. New York, printed
for the author by Clayton & Kingsland, 1818-
5.95 LoC   968

Hulett, Florence M. (RC-38)--A quantitative and qualita-
tive study of facilities for school camping and outdoor
education on state owned lands in Illinois. 1960.
Thesis (Ed.D.), Univ. of Oregon. 133p. 1.65 O   969

Hundley, Daniel Robinson (S-B4)--Social relations in
our southern states. New York, H.B. Price, 1860.
...367p. 3.95 LoC   970

Hunter, John Dunn (P&R-2)--Manners and customs of
several Indian tribes located west of the Mississippi;
... 5.95 LoC   971

Hurlstone & Walmsley (LR-E&W)--Exchequer. 1v.
(1840-41). MMP   972

Hutchins, Thomas (TOS-2)--An historical narrative
and topographical description of Louisiana and West-
Florida, ... etc. ... Philadelphia, printed for the
author, 1784. 5.95 LoC   973

--------(KC-11)--A topographical description of Virginia,
Pennsylvania, Maryland, and North Carolina; re-
printed from the original edition of 1778; ed. by
Frederick Charles Hicks. Cleveland, The Burrows
Brothers Co., 1904. 143p. 3.06 LoC   974

Hyskell Fam.--Early Heiskells and Hyskells, first
seven generations in America. By Ira D. Hyskell.
New York, 1958. 55p. 1.10 GML   975

                              I

Iliff, J. Edgar, 1852 (KC-10)--Hunter Ham; or, The outlaw's crime. New York, Beadle & Adams (1870).
102p. (Beadle's pocket novels, vol. V, no. 57)
2.61 LoC   971

Illinois State Bar Association. Quarterly bulletin.
Vols. 1-20 (1912-1932). 4.00 AB   972

Illustrirte Mittheilungen des Oberrheinischen Vereins
für Luftschiffahrt, Jahrg. 1, Nr. 1.2/3, Straszburg
1897 (Mit eigenhandigen Eintragungen des Grafen
von Zeppelin). Nr. 204-206. MK   973

Imlay, Gilbert (TOS-3)--A topographical description of
the western territory of North America; ... In a series
of letters to a friend in England. London, J. Debrett,
1792. 5.95 LoC   974

An impartial enquiry into the right of the French king to
the territory west of the great river Mississippi, in
North America (TOS-4), ... London, W. Nicoll
[1762] 5.95 LoC   975

Ingle, Edward (S-B4)--Southern sidelights; a picture of
social and economic life in the South a generation
before the war. New York, Boston, T.Y. Crowell
& Co. (1896). ...373p. 3.95 LoC   976

Ingraham, Joseph Holt (S-B3)--Bonfield: or, the Outlaw
of the Bermudas. A nautical novel. New York,
H. L. Williams (etc., etc.), 1846. 5-98p. 3.25 LoC 977

--------(S-B3)--Forrestal: or, The light of the reef. A
romance of the blue waters. New York, Morning Star
Office, 1850. 5-93p. LoC   978

--------(S-B4)--The life and adventures of Percival
Mayberry; an autobiography. Philadelphia, T.B.
Peterson (1854). ...225p. 3.95 LoC   979

--------(S-B3)--The Odd fellow; or, the secret association, and Foraging Peter. Boston, United States Pub.
Co., 1846. 35-82p. 3.25 LoC   980

--------(S-B3)--The silver ship of Mexico. A tale of
the Spanish Main. New York, H. L. Williams, 1846.
5-98p. 3.25 LoC   981

--------(S-B3)--The Spectre Steamer, and other tales.
Boston, United States Pub. Co., 1846. 9-100p.
3.25 LoC   982

--------(S-B3)--Wildash; or, The cruiser of the capes.
A nautical romance. New York, Williams Brothers,
1847. 96p. 3.25 LoC   983

--------(S-B3)--The wing of the wind. A novelette of
the sea. New York, Burgess, Stringer & Co.,
1845. 96p. 3.25 LoC   984

Ingraham, Prentiss (S-B4)--Land of legendary lore;
sketches of romance and reality on the eastern shore
of the Chesapeake. Easton, Md., The Gazette Pub.
House, 1898. 308p. 3.95 LoC   985

Irving, David (BC-3)--Lives of Scottish writers.
Edinburgh, A. & C. Black, 1850. 2v. in 1 7.50 LoC 986

--------(BC-3)--The lives of the Scottish poets, with
preliminary dissertations on the literary history of
Scotland, and early Scottish drama. 2d ed. London,
Longman, Hurst, Rees & Orme, 1810. 2v. v1, 8.04;
v2, 6.05 LoC   987

Irving, John Treat, Jr. (P&R-1)--Indian sketches, taken
during an expedition to the Pawnee Tribes. 2v. 5.95
each LoC   988

Irving, Robert Neil, Jr. (PSY-95)--Comparison of maturity,
structural, and muscular strength measures for five
somatotype categories of boys nine through fifteen
years of age. 1959. Thesis (Ed.D.), Univ. of Oregon.
256p. 2.30 O   989

Irwin, Edward Eugene--The Lamia motif in English
literature. 1.40 KU   990

Irwin, June (RC-30)--The effect of selected audio-visual
aids on teaching beginning tennis skill and knowledge
to college women. 1958. Thesis (P.E.D.), Indiana
Univ. 134p. 1.50 O   991

Isis. Vols. 1-8 (1913-1926). per vol, 5.00 C   992

Ives, Joseph Christmas (P&R-2)--Report upon the Colorado
River of the West, explored in 1857 and 1858 ...
under the direction of the Office of Explorations
and Surveys, A.A. Humphreys, Captain Topographical
Engineers, in charge. 5.95 LoC   993

J

J.R. (TOS-4)--The port-folio; or a view of the manners
and customs of various countries; ... in letters to a
friend ... London, printed by Dean & Schulze ... for
T. Egerton, Whitehall, 1812. 2v. 5.95 each LoC   994

James, Francis Bakewell (AP-1)--McCook's brigade at
the assault upon Kenesaw Mountain, Ga., June 27, 1864.
N.p., 1896. 23p. 2.45 LoC   995

James, Uriah Pierson (OV-A5)--The Negro melodist:
containing a great variety of the most popular airs,
songs, and melodies, ... Cincinnati, H.M. Bulison;
... 1857. 120p. 3.31 LoC   996

Janson, Charles William (TOS-3)--The Stranger in America:
... London, printed for James Cundee [1807] 5.95
LoC   997

Jaquith, James (TOS-3)--A history of the different manners
and customs of different parts of the United States of
America, ... N.p., n.d. 5.95 LoC   998

Jarman, Boyd O. (PSY-85)--Academic achievement of
boys nine, twelve, and fifteen years of age as related
to various strength and growth measures. 1959.
Thesis (M.S.), Univ. of Oregon. 63p. 1.05 O   999

Jay, John, 1817 (AP-1)--The Great Issue. An address
delivered before the Union Campaign Club, of East
Brooklyn, New York, on ... Oct. 25, 1864. New
York, Baker & Godwin, printers, 1864. 31p. 2.45
LoC   1000

Jefferson, Thomas (P&R-1)--Message from the President
of the United States, communicating discoveries made
in exploring the Missouri, ... by Captains Lewis and
Clark, ... with a statistical account of the countries
adjacent. Feb. 19, 1806. 5.95 LoC   1001

------- (TOS-4)--Notes on the state of Virginia; written
in the year 1781, ... for the use of a foreigner ...
1782. [Paris, printed 1784-85] 5.95 LoC   1002

--------(P&R-2)--President's message. Yesterday,
... by his Secretary to both Houses of Congress, the
following Message: (Baltimore) American -- Extra.
Wednesday morning, ... Dec. 3, 1806. 5.95 LoC 1003

Jenner, Edward, 1749-1823 (HS-1)--An inquiry into the
causes and effects of the Variolae Vaccinae. 2d ed.
London, printed for the author by S. Low, 1800.
182p. illus. 3.49 LoC   1004

Jesseph, Margaret Joyce (PE-377)--The effect of motor
ability classification in physical education on achievement and attitude of high school girls. 1956. Thesis
(M.A.), Univ. of California. 18p. .85 O   1005

Johnson, Robert (TOS-4)--The new life of Virginia:
declaring the former svccesse and present estate of
that plantation, ... London, imprinted by F. Kyngston
for W. Welby, 1612. 5.95 LoC   1006

        Johnson, Tom (pseud.)--See Green, Warren

Johnson, Thomas, of Kentucky (KC-14)--O rare Tom
Johnson, Kentucky's first poet, who, a century before
Masters, wrote his own Spoon River anthology--The
Kentucky miscellany ... with an exasperating aside
by John Wilson Townsend. Lexington, Bluegrass
Bookshop, 1949. 36p. 3.95 LoC   1007

Johnston, Albert Sidney, 1803-1862 (AP-1)--History of
Gen. Albert Sidney Johnston. New York, Knapp &
Co., c1888. 15p. 2.45 LoC   1008

Johnston, Elizabeth Bryant, 1833 (KC-13)--The days that
are no more. New York, London, (etc.), The Abbey
Press (c1901). 244p. 3.95 LoC   1009

Johnston, Elizabeth (Lichtenstein) (TOS-4)--Recollections
  of a Georgia loyalist... written in 1836; ed. by A.W.
  Eaton ... New York & London, Mansfield & Co. [1901]
  5.95 LoC   1010

Johnston, Gideon (TOS-1)--Carolina chronicle; ...
  Ed. with an introd. and notes by F.J. Klingberg.
  Berkeley & Los Angeles, Univ. of California Press,
  1946. 5.95 LoC   1011

Johnston, Maxine (ACRL-110)--Public and college library
  personnel in Texas, 1955; distribution, demand and
  personnel practices. 1958. Thesis (M.L.S.),
  Univ. of Texas. 2.25 UR   1012

Johnston, Richard Malcolm (S-B4)--Mr. Absalom Billingslea,
  and other Georgia folk. New York, Harper & Brothers,
  1888. vii, 414p. 3.95 LoC   1013

--------(S-B3)--Old times in middle Georgia. New
  York, The Macmillan Co., 1897. 249p. 3.25 LoC 1014

--------(S-B4)--Pearce Amerson's will ... with illus.
  by Orson Lowell. Chicago, Way & Williams, 1898.
  ...275p. 3.95 LoC   1015

--------(S-B4)--The Primes and their neighbors: ten
  tales of middle Georgia. New York, D. Appleton
  & Co., 1891. 310p. 3.95 LoC   1016

Johnston, William, 1804 (AP-1)--An address on the
  aspect of national affairs and the right of secession.
  Cincinnati, Rickey & Carroll, 1861. 42p. 2.45 LoC1017

Jones, Calvin (TOS-1)--A description of Weir's cave, in
  Augusta county, Virginia, ... Albany, printed and sold
  by Henry C. Southwick, 1815. 5.95 LoC   1018

Jones, Charles A. (OV-A5)--The outlaw, and other poems.
  Cincinnati, J. Drake, 1835. 72p. 2.78 LoC   1019

Jones, Charles Colcock (S-B4)--Memorial history of
   Augusta, Georgia; from its settlement in 1735 to the
   close of the 18th century ... from the close of the
   18th century to the present time by Salem Dutcher.
   Syracuse, D. Mason & Co., 1890. 512, 57p. 3.95
   LoC   1020

--------Negro myths from the Georgia coast told in the
   vernacular. Boston & New York, Houghton & Mifflin,
   1888. x, 171p. 3.95 LoC   1021

Jones, Hugh (TOS-4)--The present state of Virginia.
   Giving a particular and short account of the Indian,
   English and Negroe inhabitants of that colony. ...
   London, printed for J. Clarke, 1724. 5.95 LoC   1022

Jones, John Beauchamp (S-B3)--Adventures of Col.
   Gracchus Vanderbomb, of Sloughcreek, in pursuit
   of the presidency; also the exploits of Mr. Numerius
   Plutarch Kipps, his private secretary. Philadelphia,
   A. Hart, 1852. 19-202p. 3.25 LoC   1023

--------(S-B4)--Border war; a tale of disunion. New
   York, Rudd & Carleton, 1859. ...502p. 3.95
   LoC   1024

--------(S-B4)--A rebel war clerk's diary at the Confederate states capital. Philadelphia, J.B. Lippincott
   & Co., 1866. 2v. 3.95 LoC   1025

--------(S-B3)--The rival belles; or, Life in Washington.
   Philadelphia, T.B. Peterson & Brothers (c1878).
   15-270p. 3.25 LoC   1026

--------(S-B4)--Rural sports; a tale, in four parts.
   Philadelphia, C. Marshall, 1849. ...43p. 3.95
   LoC   1027

Jones, Laban, 1796 (KC-13)--A brief memoir of the
   Rev. Samuel Ayres Noel, ... with sermons on
   important practical subjects. Louisville, C.C. Hull
   & Brothers, printers, 1846. 436p. 6.39 LoC   1028

   Josephus, Jr. (pseud.)--See Barry, Joseph, 1828?

Journal fur Praktische Chemie. Vols. 1-162 (1870-
1943). 396.00   MXT   1029

Journal of Abnormal and Social Psychology. Vols.
1-37 (1906-1942). 171.00   C   1030

Journal of Animal Science. Vols. 1-11 (1942-1951).
49.50   C   1031

Journal of Applied Psychology. Vols. 1-26 (1917-
1942). 158.00   C   1032

Journal of Biological Chemistry. Vols. 1-59 (1905-
Apr. 1924). Index 1/50. 268.00; vols. 109-180
(Apr. 1935-1949). 387.00   C   1033

Journal of Consulting Psychology. Vols. 1-11 (1937-
1947). 37.00   C   1034

Journal of Economic Entomology. Vol. 34. 5.50 C   1035

Journal of Economic History. Vols. 1-17 (1941-1957).
60.00   C   1036

Journal of Experimental Education. Vols. 1-20
(1933-1952). 65.00   C   1037

Journal of Experimental Psychology. Vols. 1-29
(1916-1941). 160.00 C   1038

Journal of Farm Economics. Vols. 1-5 (1919-1923).
12.50   C   1039

Journal of Geomorphology. Vols. 1-5 (1938-1942).
per vol, 3.00 C   1040

Journal of Infectious Diseases. (1959-   ). 2.00
per vol. F   1041

Journal of Paleontology. Vols. 1-30. in prep   C   1042

Journal of Parasitology. Vols. 14-32 (1928-1946).
91.00 C   1043

Journal of Personality. Vols. 1-17. in prep C   1044

Journal of Philosophy. Vols. 1-20 (1904-1923).
　100.00 C   1045

Journal of Sedimentary Petrology. Vols. 1-19 (1931-
　49), 97.50; vols. 20-24 (1950-1954), 27.50 C   1046

Journal of the Aeronautical Sciences. Vols. 1-5
　(1934-1938). per vol., 5.50 C   1047

Journal of the Marine Biological Association, 1887-
　1913. complete, 31.10. (also available in units)
　MMe   1048

Journey from New Orleans to California (P&R-2).
　Chambers' Journal of Popular Literature. 5.95
　LoC   1049

Joutel, Henri (TOS-1)--Journal historique du dernier
　voyage que feu M. de la Sale fit dans le golfe de
　Mexique, pour trouver l'embouchure, & le cours de
　la riviere de Missicipi, nommée à present la
　riviere de Sanit Loüis, qui traverse la Louisiane.
　... Redige & mis en ordre par M. de Michel.
　Paris, E. Robinet, 1713. 5.95 LoC   1050

Joyce (LR-E&W)--Ecclesiastical. 1v. (1865-81).
　MMP   1051

Joyce, James--Complete works. Ed. by Herbert
　Cahoon. approx. 100.00 RDX   1052

The Juridical Review. 1st series, published by
　Wm. Green & Sons, Edinburgh. Vol. 1-67
　(1889-1955). 80.00 (225.00) MMP   1053

Jürrns, J.F.--Grondig onderwys in de gregoriaansche
　choorzang of choraal. Amsterdam, 1789. 1.00 UR 1054

Kaiserer, J.--Uber meine Erfindung einen Luftballon
durch Adler zu regieren. Wien, 1801. Nr. 202.
MK   1055

Kammeyer, Shirley Joice (RC-44)--The development of
an aptitude inventory and rating scale for community
recreation leaders. 1959. Thesis (Ph.D.), State
Univ. of Iowa. 163p. 1.90 O   1056

Kane, Paul (P&R-1)--Wanderings of an artist among the
Indians of North America, ... 5.95 LoC   1057

Kane, Thomas Leiper (P&R-2)--The Mormons. A
discourse delivered before the Historical Society of
Penna., March 26, 1850. 5.95 LoC   1058

Kausch, Johann Joseph--Psychologische abhandlung uber
den einfluss der tone und ins besondere der musik
auf die seele. Bresslau, 1782. 2.00 UR   1059

Kay, Carolyn (ACRL-114)--Research training at the master's
degree level in A.L.A.-accredited library schools,
1956. 1956. Thesis (M.L.S.), Univ. of Texas.
1.50 UR   1060

Keans & Grant's Appeals (LR-E&W)--Registration.
1v. (1854-62). MMP   1061

Keen, John S. (KC-14)--Memoir of F.W. Henck,
with notes and comments. Highway, Ky., Bible
Advocate Print, 1899. ...247p. 3.95 LoC   1062

Keeney, Clifford Emerson (PH-67)--The relationship in
white rats between changes in work capacity due to
training and the eosinophil response to muscular
exercise. 1959. Thesis (Ph.D.), New York Univ.
114p. 1.65 O   1063

Keep, G.R.C.--The Irish emigration to North America
in the second half of the nineteenth century. Thesis
(Ph.D.). 2.15 MMe   1064

Keith, George (TOS-4)--A Journal of travels from New-
Hampshire to Caratuck, ...London, Joseph Downing
for Brab. Aylmer, 1706. 5.95 LoC   1065

Kelley, William Darrah, 1814 (AP-1)--Addresses of
Hon. W.D. Kelley, Miss Anna E. Dickinson, and Mr.
Frederick Douglas, at a mass meeting, Philadelphia,
July 6, 1863, for the promotion of colored enlistments.
Philadelphia, 1863. 8p. 2.45 LoC   1066

--------(AP-1)--The South--its resources and wants.
His address to the citizens of New Orleans. His address at Montgomery, Ala., and his address to his
constituents. Washington, Union Republican
Congressional Committee, 1866? 20p. 2.45 LoC 1067

Kelly, Samuel (TOS-1)--...An eighteenth century seaman,
whose days have been few and evil, ... New ed. with
introd. by C. Garstin; ... New York, Frederick A.
Stokes, 1925. 5.95 LoC   1068

Kemble, Frances Anne (S-B4)--Journal of a residence
on a Georgian plantation in 1838-1839. New York,
Harper & Brothers, 1863. 337p. 3.95   LoC   1069

Kendall, George Wilkins (S-B4)--The war between the
United States and Mexico illustrated, embracing
pictorial drawings of all the principal conflicts, by
Carl Nebel ... with a description of each battle by
Geo. W. Kendall. New York, D. Appleton & Co.
(etc. etc.), 1851. iv, 52p. plates 3.95 LoC   1070

Kennedy, John Pendleton (S-B3)--The border states,
their power and duty in the present disordered condition
of the country. (n.p., 1860). 46p. 3.25 LoC   1071

--------(S-B3)--Mr. Ambrose's letters on the rebellion.
New York, Hurd & Houghton; Baltimore, J.S. Waters,
1865. 246p. 3.25 LoC   1072

Kennedy, William (S-B4)--Texas: the rise, progress,
and prospects of the Republic of Texas. London,
R. Hastings, 1841. 2v. 3.95 LoC   1073

Kentucky. Bureau of agriculture, horticulture, and
statistics (KC-11)--The resources and condition of
the commonwealth of Kentucky. Frankfort, Ky.,
S.I.M. Major, public printer, 1877. 108p. 2.68
LoC   1074

Kentucky. Commissioners to the Peace Conference at
Washington, Feb. 1861 (AP-1)--Report of the Kentucky
commissioners to the late peace conference held at
Washington city, made to the legislature of Kentucky.
Frankfort, printed at the Yeoman office. J.B. Major,
state printer, 1861. 88p. 2.45 LoC   1075

Kentucky. General Assembly, 1807-1808 (KC-10)--
Mr. Rowan's motion, for an inquiry into the conduct
of Harry Innis, district judge of the United States
for the district of Kentucky. City of Washington,
A. & G. Way, printers, 1808. 54p. 2.50 LoC   1076

Kentucky. General Assembly (KC-10)--Speeches and
proceedings upon the announcement of the death of
Hon. John C. Breckinridge in the Senate and House
of Representatives of Kentucky, Friday and Saturday,
January 7th and 22d, 1876. Frankfort, Ky., Jas. A.
Hodges, 1876. 57p. 2.50 LoC   1077

Kentucky. State industrial and commercial conference,
Louisville, 1887 (KC-12)--Kentucky towns and counties.
Being reports of their growth, natural resources and
industrial improvement made to the ... conference
at Louisville, Oct. 4th, 5th and 6th, 1887. Frankfort,
Ky., Capital Book & Job Prtg. Co., 1887. 112p. 2.72
LoC   1078

--------(KC-12)--Transportation systems, together with
a review of transportation problems and opportunities
to be developed. Frankfort, Ky., Capital Prtg. Co.,
1887. 66p. 2.50 LoC   1079

Kentucky Culture Series. Eighth group of ten titles
(71-80). 29.50 LoC
The titles in this series are: 1080

        Brown, T.--Brown's three years in the Kentucky
            prisons, ...
        Espy, J.M. (also TOS-4)--Memorandums of a tour ...
        Gerstner, C.--Beschreibung einer reise durch
            die Vereinigten Staaten ...
        Hale, J.P.--Daniel Boone.
        Harding, B.--A tour through the Western country.
        McNemar, R.--A selection of hymns and poems.

Magnum Opus. --The great book of the Univ. of
Comus.
Rice, D. --An essay on baptism.
Thompson, C.L. --Times of refeshing.
Wilmot, F.A. --Disclosures and confesions...

Kentucky Culture Series. Ninth group of ten titles (81-
90). 29.50 LoC
The titles in this series are: 1081

Anderson, C. --Funeral oration ... on Henry Clay.
Dunlavy, J. --The manifesto, ...
Holley, H. --Discourse occasioned by the death of
Col. James Morrison, ...
McNemar, R. -- The Kentucky revival, ...
Mitchell, W.M. --The underground railroad from
slavery to freedom.
Rice, D. --A Kentucky protest against slavery.
Robertson, G. --Address ...
Stiles, J.C. --Letter of Alexander Campbell, ...
Thomas, F.W. --Sketches of character, ...
Tower, P. --Slavery unmasked: ...

Kentucky Culture Series. Tenth group of ten titles
(91-100). 29.50 LoC
The titles in this series are: 1082

Bailey, G. --The great caverns of Kentucky: ...
Baldwin, T., 1750? ---Massacre of wife and children...
Bramlette, T.E., 1817--Speech ...
Ely, W. --The Big Sandy Valley.
Forwood, W.S., 1830--... Mammoth Cave of
Kentucky.
Iliff, J.E., 1852--Hunter Ham; ...
Kentucky. General Assembly. --Speeches and
proceedings ...
Kentucky. General Assembly, 1807-1808. --
Mr. Rowan's motion, ...
Martin, H. --Pictorial atlas to the Mammoth Cave, ...
Taney, M.F. --Kentucky pioneer women, ...

Kentucky Culture Series. Eleventh group of ten titles
(101-110). 29.50 LoC
The titles in this series are: 1083

Gould, E.W., 1811--Fifty years on the Mississippi.

Hovey, H.C., 1833--Mammoth Cave of Kentucky; ...
Hutchins, T., 1730--Topographical description of
    Virginia, ...
Kentucky. Bureau of agriculture, horticulture,
    and statistics.--The resources and condition of
    the commonwealth of Kentucky.
Kottenkamp, F.J., 1806--Die ersten Amerikaner
    in Westen.
Mori, S.--Zwei briefe aus Amerika.
St. John, P.B., 1821--Queen of the woods; ...
Smith, H.C.--Outline history of the wilderness of
    Kentucky ...
Triplett, T.--To the public.
Witherspoon, P.F.--Through two administrations, ...

Kentucky Culture Series. Twelfth group of ten titles
    (111-120). 29.50 LoC
The titles in this series are:

    Binkerd, A.D.--Pictorial guide to the Mammoth
        Cave, Kentucky.
    Devol, G.H.--Forty years a gambler on the
        Mississippi.
    Dixon. S.H., 1855--Robert Warren, the Texas
        refugee.
    Hawks, F.L., 1798--Adventures of Daniel Boone, ...
    Kentucky. State industrial and commercial conference,
        Louisville, 1887.--Kentucky towns and counties.
    Kentucky. State industrial and commercial conference,
        Louisville, 1887.-- Transportation systems, ...
    Packard, A.S., 1839--The Mammoth Cave and its
        inhabitants, ...
    Safford, W.H., 1821--Life of Harman Blennerhassett.
    Willett, E., 1830--Old Honesty; ...
    Willett, E., 1830--The Shawnee scout; ...

Kentucky Culture Series. Thirteenth group of ten titles
    (121-130). 29.50 LoC
The titles in this series are: 1085

    Ayres & Givens, firm, Louisville.--Eastern
        Kentucky, a field for profitable investment.
    Bowling Green and Warren County immigration
        society, Bowling Green, Ky.--A condensed,
        accurate and fair description of the resources...

108

Drake, D., 1785--Pioneer life in Kentucky.
Drake, D., 1785--A systematic treatise, ... on the
    principal diseases of the interior valley of
    North America, ...
Fernow, B., 1837--The Ohio valley in colonial days.
History of the Ohio falls cities and their counties, ...
Johnston, E.B., 1833--The days that are no more.
Jones, L. 1796--Brief memoir of the Rev. S.A.
    Noel, ...
Macfarland, W.H.--Discourse on the life of Hon.
    Henry Clay.
Mansfield, E.D., 1801--Memoirs of Daniel Drake, ...

Kentucky Culture Series. Fourteenth group of sixty titles
    (131-190). Group price, 2.95 per vol. LoC
The titles in this series are: 1086

Bagg, L.H., 1846--Ten thousand miles on a bicycle.
Bancroft, A.C.--Life and death of Jefferson Davis, ...
Combs, L., 1793--Col. Wm. Dudley's defeat
    opposite Fort Meigs.
Clay, C.M.--Appeal ... to Kentucky and the world.
De Moss, J.C.--Short history of ... W.F. Corbin, ...
Dunlavy, J., 1769--The manifesto, ...
Edwards, J.E., 1814--Life of Rev. John Wesley
    Childs: ...
Errett, I., 1820--Life and writings of George E.
    Flower.
Fairbank, C., 1816--...During slavery times.
Flagg, E., 1815--The far West; ...
Franklin, J., 1834--Life and times of Benjamin
    Franklin.
Frost, J., 1800--Life of Major Gen. Zachary Taylor;
Fry, J.B., 1827--Operations of the army under
    Buell ...
Green, W.--A blue-grass thoroughbred.
Gross, S.D., 1805, ed.--Lives of eminent American
    physicians and surgeons of the 19th century.
Hockersmith, L.D., 1833--Morgan's escape.
Howe, H., 1816--The times of rebellion in the West:..
Johnson, T., of Ky.--O rare Tom Johnson, ...
Keen, J.S.--Memoir of F.W. Henck, ...
La Bree, B., ed.--Camp fires of the Confederacy; ...
Latrobe, C.J., 1801--The rambler in North America.
Liberty saved, ...

McDowell, Mrs. K.S., 1849--Dialect tales.
McLaughlin, J.F., 1839--Matthew Lyon, ...
Meigs, C.D., 1792--A biographical notice of Daniel
  Drake, ...
Muhlenberg, H.A., 1823--Life of Major-Gen.
  Peter Muhlenberg ...
Norton, J.N., 1820--Life of Bishop Ravenscroft.
Ord, G., 1781--...Life of Alexander Wilson, ...
Palmer, J.M., 1817--Personal recollections.
Parker, A.--The real Madeleine Pollard.
Peirce, B.K., 1819--Life in the woods; ...
Pomfrey, J.W.--...Exposition of the Knights of
  the golden circle, ...
Rafinesque, C.S.--Alsographia Americana, ...
Rafinesque, C.S.--American manual of the grape vines
Rafinesque, C.S.--American manual of the mulberry
  trees.
Rafinesque, C.S.--The American nations; ...
Rafinesque, C.S.--Analyse de la nature; ...
Rafinesque, C.S.--The ancient monuments of North
  and South America.
Rafinesque, C.S.--Annals of nature; ...
Rafinesque, C.S.--Caratteri di alouni nuovi generi e
  nuove specie de animali e piante della Sicilia...
Rafinesque, C.S.--Celestial wonders and philosophy,..
Rafinesqqe, C.S.--Circular address on botany and
  zoology.
Rafinesque, C.S.--Genius and spirit of the Hebrew
  Bible.
Rafinesque, C.S.--The good book, and amenities of
  nature, ...
Rafinesque, C.S.--Improvements of universities,
  colleges, ...
Rafinesque, C.S.--Indice d'ittiologia siciliana ossia
  catalogo ...
Rafinesque, C.S.--Monograph of the fluviatile bivalve
  shells of the river Ohio, ...
Rafinesque, C.S.--Neogenyton, ...
Rafinesque, C.S.--Outlines of a general history of
  North America.
Rafinesque, C.S.--Sylva telluriana.
Rafinesque, C.S.--The world, or Instability. A poem.
Read, O.P.--A Kentucky Colonel.
Smith, Eli, 1787--Funeral sermon on the death of
  Gov. Madison, ...

Speed, T., 1841--Who fought the battle.
Thomas, D., 1732--The observer trying the great
    reformation ...
Tuttle, C.R., 1848--...Border wars of two centuries,
Watterson, H., 1840--George Dennison (sic) Prentice.
Victor, W.B.--Life and events.

Ker, Henry (TOS-3)--Travels through the western interior
    of the United States, from the year 1808 up to the year
    1816. ...Elizabethtown, N.J., printed for the author,
    1816. 5.95 LoC   1087

Kessell, Johann C.B.--Unterricht im general-basse zum
    gebrauche fur lehrer und lernende. Leipzig, 1791.
    1.25 UR   1088

Keyes, James (MFM)--Pioneers of Scioto County. 1880.
    121p. 2.82 LoC   1089

Kimber, Edward (TOS-1)--A relation, or Journal of a
    late expedition to the gates of St. Augustine, ...conducted
    by ... General James Oglethorpe, ... London,
    T. Astley, 1744. 5.95 LoC   1090

Kincaid, Donald (PE-438)--The specificity of muscular
    endurance following different rates of training. 1959.
    Thesis (M.S.), Pennsylvania State Univ. 57p. 1.15
    O   1091

King, A. (AP-1)--British sympathy in the American
    crisis. By an Irishman. Dublin, printed by Porteous
    &Gibbs, 1863. 15p. 2.45 LoC   1092

King, Richard (P&R-2)--Narrative of a journey to the
    shores of the Arctic Ocean, in 1833-35; ... 2v.
    5.95 each   LoC   1093

King, Shirley (PE-390)--Relaxation and stress. 1958.
    Thesis (M.Ed.), Woman's College, Univ. of North
    Carolina. 106p. 1.40 O   1094

King, William Howard, Jr. (PSY-86)--A time and motion
    study of competitive backstroke swimming turns. 1956.
    Thesis (Ed.D.), Boston Univ. 101p. 1.25 O   1095

Kingdom, William, Jr. (TOS-2)--America and the
British colonies. An abstract of all the most useful
information relative to the United States, ... London,
printed for G. & W. B. Whitaker, 1820. 5.95 LoC   1096

Kingman Fam.--Descendants of Henry Kingman. Some
early generations. By Bradford Kingman. Boston,
1912. 96p. 1.40 GML   1097

Kingsbury, L. L.--The philosophical influences bearing
on Alexander Campbell and the beginnings of the
Disciples of Christ movement. Thesis (Ph.D.).
1.10.6 MMe   1098

Kirby--Simplicissimus as an index of Grimmelshausen's
concept of the world and his place in the baroque era.
1.40 KU   1099

Kirchner, Glenn (PE-391)--The construction of a battery
of tests designed to measure strength, endurance,
power and speed among elementary school-age boys.
1959. Thesis (Ed.D.), Univ. of Oregon. 106p.
1.40 O   1100

Kirker, James (P&R-1)--Don Santiago Kirker, the Indian
fighter. 5.95 LoC   1101

Kirnberger, Johann Philipp--Anleitung zur singe-komposi-
tion. Berlin, 1782. 1.60 UR   1102

--------Gedanken uber die verschiedenen lehrarten in
der komposition. Wien [1782] 1.00 UR   1103

--------Die wahren grundsatze zum gebrauch der
harmonie. Berlin & Konigsberg, 1773. 1.60 UR   1104

Klein, Walter Casper (HE-55)--A health knowledge and
understanding test for fifth grade pupils. 1958.
Thesis (D. of Health & Safety), Indiana Univ. 155p.
1.90 O   1105

Kleindienst, Viola K. (RC-31)--A study of the experiences of camping for the purpose of pointing out ways in which a school camp program may supplement the elementary school at the sixth grade level. 1957. Thesis (Ed.D.), New York Univ. 209p. 2.10 O   1106

Kleukens, Ch.H. und J. Goebel--Schrift, Letter, Mikrokopie.-Mainzer Presse. Mainz, 1940. Nr.126. MK1107

Kleukens, Christian--Reinke Voss. Mit Bildern von F.W.Kleukens. Darmstadt, 1913. Nr.341-344. MK1108

Knapp & Ombler (LR-E&W)--Election. 1v. (1834-35). MMP   1109

Knight, Henry Cogswell (TOS-2)--Letters from the South and West; by Arthur Singleton (pseud.). Boston, pub. by Richardson & Lord, J.H.A. Frost, printer, 1824. 5.95 LoC   1110

Knight Gen.--Typewritten ms. of the Knight gen. With typed index. 428p. 3.50 GML   1111

Koch, Heinrich Christoph--Versuch einer anleitung zur composition. Leipzig, 1782-93. 9.25   UR   1112

Kottenkamp, Franz Justus, 1806 (KC-11)--Die ersten Amerikaner in Westen. Daniel Boone und seine gefahrten. (Die grundung Kentucky's Tecumseh und dessen Bruder.) Zweite ausgabe mit acht colorirten bildern. Stuttgart, Verlag von Schmidt & Spring, 1858. 540p. 7.43 LoC   1113

Kreipe--A translation of Milton's "Samson Agonistes." 1.05 KU   1114

Kron, Karl (pseud.)--See Bagg, Lyman Hotchkiss

Kutzing, F.T.--Tablulae phycologicae. 42.00 F   1115

L.E., (AP-1)--Notes on American affairs. London,
Houlston & Wright, 1863. 30p. 2.45 LoC   1116

Laborde, Jean Benjamin de--Essai sur la musique
ancienne et moderne. Paris, 1780. 19.75 UR   1117

Laboulaye, Edouard Rene Lefebvre de, 1811 (AP-1)--
Why the North cannot consent to disunion. Reprinted
from the New York Tribune. Edinburgh, Murray
& Gibb, printers, 1863. 14p. 2.45 LoC   1118

La Bree, Benjamin, ed. (KC-14)--Camp fires of the
Confederacy; a volume of humorous anecdotes, reminis-
cences, deeds of heroism, ... Confederate poems.
Ed. by Ben La Bree. Louisville, Ky., Courier-
Journal Job Prtg. Co., 1898. 560p. illus. 3.95
LoC   1119

La Croix, A. Phérotée de--L'art de la poisie Francoise
et Latine, avec une idee de la musique sous une
nouvelle methode. Lyon, 1694. 4.00 UR   1120

Lade, Robert (Antoine Francois Prevost-d'Exiles) (TOS-4)--
Voyages du Capitaine Robert Lade en differentes partes
de l'Afrique, de l'Asie, et de l'Amérique: ... Paris,
1744. 2v. 5.95 each LoC   1121

Lafayette, Marie Joseph Paul Yves Roch Gilbert du
Motier, Marquis de (TOS-1)--The memoirs, corres-
pondence, and manuscripts of Marquis de Lafayette.
Pub. by his family. London & New York, Saunders
& Otley, 1837. 3v. 5.95 each LoC   1122

La Feillée, Francois de -- Methode nouvelle pour apprendre
parfaitement les regles du plain-chant. Poitiers,
1773. 3.20 UR   1123

LaFleche, Richer (P&R-2)--Lettre ... missionaire, à
un de ses amis. Saint Francois de la Prairie du
Cheval-Blanc, le 4 Septembre, 1851. [Included also
with Association de la Propagation de la Foi] 5.95
LoC   1124

La Harpe, Bernard de (TOS-1)--Journal historique de
l'etablissement des Francais a la Louisiane, Paris,
Nouvelle-Orleans (Etats Unis), A. L. Boinare, Libraire-
Editeur. Paris, Hector Hossange, Libraire. Quai
Voltaire, No. 11, 1831. 5.95   LoC   1125

Lahontan, Louis Armand de Lom d'Arce, Baron de
(TOS-4)--Nouveauz Voyages de Mr. Le Baron de
Lahontan, dans l'Amérique Septentrionale, Qui
continnent une Relation des differens Peuples qui y
habitent; ... A la Haye, Chez les Freres l'honore ...
1703. 2v. 5.95 each   LoC   1126

Laing, David, ed. (BC-3)--Early popular poetry of
Scotland and the northern border ... rearranged and
rev. with additions and a glossary, by W. Carew Hazlitt.
London, Reeves & Turner, 1895. 2v. v1, 7.27;
v2, 5.28   LoC   1127

Lambert, John (TOS-2)--Travels through lower Canada,
and the United States of North America, in the years,
1806-08. To which are added, biographical notices
and anecdotes of some of the leading characters of the
United States. ... London, printed for Richard Phillips,
1810. 3v. 5.95 each LoC   1128

Lamm, Jesse M. (RC-45)--A manual for the adminis-
tration of recreation programs for mentally defective
children in state institutions for mental defectives.
1959. Thesis (Ed.D.), New York Univ. 153p.
1.90 O   1129

Landolphe, Jean Francois (TOS-1)--Memoires ...
Paris, A. Bertrand [etc.] 1823. 2v. 5.95 each LoC 1130

Langlé,Honoré Francois M.--Traite d'harmonie et de
modulation. Paris, 1797. 2.25 UR   1131

--------Traite de la basse sous le chant, precede de
toutes les regles de la composition. Paris [1798]
4.90 UR   1132

Langworthy, Franklin (P&R-1)--Scenery of the plains,
mountains and mines: or a diary kept upon the overland
route to California, ... in the years 1850-53 5.95
LoC   1133

Lanier, Gene D. (ACRL-98)--The library and television.
.50 UR   1134

Larned, J.M.--The literature of American history.
5.00   SM   1135

La Rochefoucauld-Liancourt [et d'Estissac. Francois-
Alexandre-Frederic, Duc de] (TOS-3)--Voyage dans
les Etats-Unis d'Amerique, fait en 1795, ...1797.
Paris, DuPont, Buisson, Charles Pougens, 1799.
8v. 5.95 each LoC   1136

Latrobe, Charles Joseph, 1801 (KC-14, also P&R-1)--
The rambler in North America, 1832-33. New York,
Harper & Brothers, 1835. 2v. 5.95 each LoC   1137

Laudonnière, René Goulaine de (TOS-4)--L'histoire
notable de la Floride située ès Indes Occidentales,
... mise en lumière par M. Basanier (ed.). Paris,
M. Basanier, 1586. 5.95 LoC   1138

Laval, Antoine Jean de (TOS-2)--Voyage de la Louisiane,
... Paris, J. Mariette, 1728. 5.95 LoC   1139

La Voye Mignot, de--Traite de mvsiqve. Paris, 1656.
1.50   UR   1140

Lawson, John (TOS-4)--A new voyage to Carolina; containing the exact description and natural history of
that country; ... London, printed in the year 1709.
5.95   LoC   1141

Lawson, Patricia A. (PE-392)--An analysis of a group of
motor fitness tests which purport to measure agility
as they apply to elementary school girls. 1959.
Thesis (M.A.), Univ. of Oregon. 63p. 1.15 O   1142

Leatham, E.A. (AP-1)--Speech ... upon American
affairs. Huddersfield, J. Woodhead, printer, 1862.
20p. 2.45 LoC   1143

Lederer, John (TOS-4)--The discoveries of John
   Lederer in three several marches from Virginia, to
   the west of Carolina, and other parts of the continent:
   ... Collected and trans. out of Latine from his
   discourse and writings, by Sir William Talbot.
   London, printed by J.C. for S. Heyrick, 1672. 5.95
   LoC   1144

Ledyard, J.--Journal of Capt. Cook's last voyage to
   the Pacific Ocean. 2.50 SM   1145

Lee, Daniel and Joseph H. Frost (P&R-1)--Ten years
   in Oregon. 5.95 LoC   1146

Lee, Nelson (P&R-2)--Three years among the Camanches.
   5.95 LoC   1147

Legare, James Matthews (S-B3)--Orta-undis, and other
   poems. Boston, W.D. Ticknor & Co., 1848. 102p.
   3.25 LoC   1148

Lehman, Alice Ethel (PE-378)-- An analysis of the
   performance of junior high school girls in 14 physical
   fitness tests. 1958. Thesis (M.S.), Oregon State
   College. 67p. 1.05 O   1149

Leidy, Joseph (P&R-2)--Notice of remains of extinct
   Vertebrata, from the Valley of the Niobrara River.
   5.95 LoC   1150

Leland, Alonzo (P&R-1)--New map of the mining regions
   of Oregon and Washington Territory; together with
   a sketch of the mines; ... Comp. from observations
   made in 1861-62. 5.95 LoC   1151

Leland, Charles Godfrey, 1824 (AP-1)--Ye book of
   copperheads. Philadelphia, F. Leypoldt, ... 24p.
   2.45 LoC   1152

Lemery, Nicolas, 1645-1715 (HS-1)--Cours de chymie.
   2 ed., rev., corr. & augm. par l'autheur. Paris,
   Chez l'autheur, 1677. 584p. 7.91 LoC   1153

Lemon, Berlan (HE-41)--Parental attitudes toward sex
   education. 1948. Thesis (M.S.), Univ. of Oregon.
   73p. 1.25 O   1154

Leng, Sir William Christopher (AP-1)--The American war: the aims, antecedent, and principles of the belligerent. Dundee, printed at the Adviser Office, 1863. 38p. 2.45 LoC   1155

Letters on emigration (TOS-1). By a gentleman, lately returned from America. London, C. & G. Kearsley, 1794. 5.95 LoC   1156

Levasseur, Auguste (TOS-4)--Lafayette en Amerique, en 1824-25, ou, Journal d'un voyage aux Etats-Unis, ... Paris, Baudoin, 1829. 2v. 5.95 each LoC   1157

Lewis--George Orwell: the man and his work. .70 KU1158

Lewis, Barbara Irene (PE-439)--The relationship of selected factors to the vertical jump. 1959. Thesis (M.A.), State Univ. of Iowa. 41p. 1.15 O   1159

Lewis, O.F.--Development of American prisons and prison customs, 1776-1845. 2.75 SM   1160

Lewis and Clark (P&R-1)--History of the expedition under the command of Capts. Lewis & Clark, to the sources of the Missouri, ... Performed during the years 1804-06. 2v. 5.95 each LoC   1161

Lewis and Clark (P&R-1)--The travels of Capts. Lewis & Clarke, ... performed in the years 1804-1806, being upwards of three thousand miles from St. Louis, ... to the Pacifik Ocean; ... Comp. from various authentic sources and documents... 5.95 LoC   1162

Liberty saved, or the warnings of an old Kentuckian to his fellow-citizens on the danger of electing partisans of the old Court of Appeals (KC-14). Louisville, Ky., W. Tanner, printer, 1825. ...28p. 3.95 LoC   1163

Little, Robert Weaver, ed.--Flameproofing textile fabrics. 1947. ACS monograph no. 104. 12.95 MXT   1164

Lloyd & Welsby (LR-E&W)--Commercial.1v. (1829-30). MMP   1165

Lockwood, Joe Bosley (PE-379)--Physical fitness and
physical education programs in selected schools of
South Dakota. 1958. Thesis (M.S.), South Dakota
State College. 90p. 1.25 O   1166

Loftin, Aimee M. (PSY-115)--Effects of variations in
method and club progression on golf achievement of
college women. 1957. Thesis (Ed.D.), Indiana
Univ. 181p. 1.90 O   1167

Long, Alexander, 1816 (AP-1)--Speech ... in the Federal
House of Representatives ... on 7th April, 1864,
on the subject of the recognition of the south. Glasgow,
Wm. Love, 1864? 16p. 2.45 LoC   1168

Lorain, John (TOS-4)--Hints to emigrants, or a
comparative estimate of the advantage of Pennsylvania,
and of the western territory, etc. Philadelphia, pub.
by Littell & Henry, A. Waldie, printer, 1819. 5.95
LoC   1169

Lorenzoni, Antonio--Saggio per ben sonare il flautotraverso.
Vincenza, 1779. 1.25 UR   1170

        Louisianais, M. (pseud.)--See Mercier, Alfred

Lounsbury, T.R.--Studies in Chaucer. 3v. 10.00
SM   1171

Lowell, Daniel W. & Co. (P&R-2)--Map of the Nez
Perces and Salmon River gold mines in Washington
Territory. 5.95 LoC   1172

Lowndes, Maxwell & Pollock (LR-E&W)--Bail. 2v.
(1850-51). MMP   1173

Lowndes & Maxwell (LR-E&W)--Bail. 1v. (1852-54).
MMP   1174

Lucas,Daniel Bedinger (S-B4)--The wreath of Eglantine,
and other poems, ed. and in part composed by D.B.
Lucas. Baltimore, Kelly, Piet & Co., 1869. 169p.
illus. 3.95 LoC   1175

Luder's Cases (LR-E&W)--Election. 3v. (1784-87).
  MMP   1176

Lutwyche (LR-E&W)--Registration. 2v. (1843-53).
  MMP   1177

                              M

McAdam, Robert Everett (PH-65)--An investigation of
  the effects of physical training on cardiovascular
  components in the adult male. 1955. Thesis (Ph.D.),
  Univ. of Illinois. 127p. 1.65 O   1178

    McArone (pseud.)--See Arnold, George, 1834.

McCabe, James Dabney (S-B3)--The aid-de-camp; a
  romance of the war. Richmond, W.A.J. Smith,
  1863. 113p. 3.25 LoC   1179

--------(S-B3)--The life of Thomas J. Jackson. By
  an ex-cadet. 2d ed. rev. & enl. by the author.
  Richmond, J.E. Goode, 1864. 196p. 3.25 LoC   1180

McCabe, William Gordon (S-B4)--The defence of Petersburg. Address ... before the Virginia division of
  the Army of Northern Virginia, at the annual meeting
  held in the Capitol at Richmond, Va., Nov. 1st,
  1876. Richmond, G.W. Gary, printer, 1876. ...52p.
  3.95 LoC   1181

McClung, J.A. (MFM, also OV-A1, KC-1)--Sketches
  of Western adventure. 1879. 3.59 LoC   1182

McCormick, Richard Cunningham (P&R-1)--Arizona:
  its resources and prospects. 5.95 LoC   1183

McCoy, Isaac (P&R-1)--History of Baptist Indian Missions:
  ... 5.95 LoC   1184

--------(P&R-1)--Remove Indians westward. 20th Cong.
  2nd Sess., H.R. Report 87. Feb. 18, 1829, Serial
  177. 5.95 LoC   1185

McCoy, Mercer Garnett (ACRL-101)--A check-list of
Norfolk, Virginia imprints from 1774 to 1876. 1954.
Thesis (M.S. in L.S.), Catholic Univ. of America.
1.50 UR   1186

M'Donell, Alexander (P&R-2)--A narrative of transactions
in the Red River Country, from the commencement
of the operations of the Earl of Selkirk, till the summer
of the year 1816. 5.95 LoC   1187

McDowell, Mrs. Katherine Sherwood (Bonner), 1849
(KC-14)--Dialect tales, by Sherwood Bonner. New
York, Harper & Brothers, 1883. 187p. 3.95 LoC   1188

Macfarland, William H. (KC-13)--Discourse on the life
of Honorable Henry Clay. Richmond, H.K. Ellyson,
printer, 1852. 15p. 2.50 LoC   1189

Mackenzie, Alexander (P&R-2)--Voyages from Montreal,
... to the Frozen and Pacific Oceans; in the years
1789 and 1793. With a preliminary account of ...
the fur trade of that country. 5.95 LoC   1190

Mackenzie, Eneas (TOS-2)--An historical, topographical,
and descriptive view of the United States of America,
... Newcastle upon Tyne, printed & pub. by Mackenzie
& Dent [1819] 5.95 LoC   1191

McKinnell, Bettina F. (ACRL-105)--A check-list of
Richmond, Virginia imprints, 1841-1852. 1956. Thesis
(M.S. in L.S.), Catholic Univ. of America. 2.25
UR   1192

McKnight, Charles (MFM)--Our Western border ... one
hundred years ago. 1875. 756p. 9.81 LoC   1193

McLaughlin, James Fairfax, 1839 (KC-14)--Matthew
Lyon, the Hampden of Congress, a biography.
New York, Wynkoop, Hellenbeck, Crawford Co.,
1900. xi, 531p. 3.95 LoC   1194

MacLean, Janet R. (RC-39)--An analysis of leisure
time activities of selected aged residents of Bartholomew
County, Indiana. 1959. Thesis (D. of Rec.), Indiana
Univ. 271p. 2.30 O   1195

McNally, Eugene Wayne (PSY-116)--Relationship of general
interests to maturity, structure, and strength of nine
through fourteen year old boys. 1960. Thesis (Ph.D.),
Univ. of Oregon. 96p. 1.40 O   1196

McNemar, Richard (KC-9)--The Kentucky revival, or,
A short history of the late extraordinary outpouring
of the spirit of God in the western states of America ...
with a brief account of the entrance and progress of
what the world calls Shakerism, among the subjects
of the late revival in Ohio and Kentucky. Cincinnati,
from the press of John W. Browne, ... 1807. 119p.
3.33 LoC   1197

--------(KC-8)--A selection of hymns and poems; for
the use of believers. ... Watetvliet (i.e. Watervliet)
O., 1833. 180p. 3.97 LoC   1198

Macrae & Hertslet (LR-E&W)--Bankruptcy. 2v. (1847-
54). MMP   1199

Macrory (LR-E&W)--Patent. 1v. (1852-55). MMP   1200

Magnum Opus (KC-8)--The great book of the University
of Comus. The pandect of our national hilaritas,
comprising essays upon the thirteen divisions of the
rituals; ... Louisville, Ky., Pub. under the direction
of the thirteen doges, 1886. 160p. 3.75 LoC   1201

Mainwaring, John--Georg Friedrich Handels lebensbeschrei-
bung; tr. by J. Mattheson. Hamburg, 1761. 1.60
UR   1202

--------Memoirs of the life of the late George Frederic
Handel. London, 1760. 2.00 UR   1203

Majer, Joseph Friedrich B.C.--Neu-eroeffneter theoretisch-
und pracktischer music-saal. Nuernberg, 1741.
1.50 UR   1204

Makemie, Francis (TOS-1)--A plain and friendly persuasive to the inhabitants of Virginia and Maryland for
  promoting towns and cohabitation. ... London,
  J. Humfreys, 1705. 5.95 LoC   1205

Malone, D.--Public life of Thomas Cooper, 1783-1839.
  2.50 SM   1206

Manning & Ryland (LR-E&W)--King's Bench. 5v.
  (1827-30). MMP   1207

Manning & Ryland (LR-E&W)--Magistrates Court. 3v.
  (1827-30). MMP   1208

Manning (Isle of Wight) (LR-E&W)--Revision. 1v.
  (1832-35). MMP   1209

Mansfield, Edward Deering, 1801 (KC-13)--Memoirs
  of the life and services of Daniel Drake, M.D.,
  physician, professor and author; with notices of the
  early settlement of Cincinnati. ... Cincinnati, Applegate
  & Co., 1855. 408p. 5.98 LoC   1210

Mansi, Giovanni Domenico--Sacrorum conciliorum nova
  et amplissima collectio. Paris, 1900-1927. 60v.
  440.00 F   1211

Marcello, Benedetto--Il teatro alla moda. [Venezia,
  17--] 1.00 UR   1212

Marcos y Navas, Francisco--Arte, o compendio general
  del canto--llano. Madrid, 1777 6.00 UR   1213

Marcou, Jules (P&R-1)--Geology of North America;
  with two reports on the prairies of Arkansas and Texas,
  the Rocky Mountains of New Mexico, and the Sierra
  Nevada of California, ... 5.95 LoC   1214

Marcy, Randolph Barnes (P&R-2)--Exploration of the
  Red River of Louisiana, in the year 1852. 5.95
  LoC   1215

--------(P&R-2)--The prairie traveller. A hand-book
  for overland expeditions. ... 5.95 LoC   1216

Marino, Frank P. (PE-440)--The relationship of foot
extension strength and jumping exercises to vertical
jumping performance. 1959. Thesis (M.S.), Pennsylvania State Univ. 54p. 1.15   O   1217

Maritime Law Cases (Crockford) (LR-E&W)--Admiralty.
3v. (1860-71). MMP   1218

Marks, Elias (S-B3)--Elfreide of Guldal, a Scandinavian
legend: and other poems. By Marks of Barhamville.
New York, D. Appleton & Co. (etc.) 1850. 9-186p.
3.25 LoC   1219

Marquette, Jacques (TOS-1)--Voyage et découverte
de quelques pays et nations de l'Amérique Septentrionale,
... Paris, Chez Estienne Michallet, 1681. 5.95 LoC
                                                    1220

Marpurg, Friedrich Wilhelm--Abhandlung von der fuge.
Berlin, 1753-54. 5.25 UR   1221

--------Anfangsgruende der theoretischen musik.
Leipzig, 1757. 2.25 UR   1222

--------Anleitung zur musik uberhaupt und zur singkunst
besonders. Berlin, 1763. 1.60 UR   1223

--------Handbuch bey dem generalbasse und der
komposition. Berlin, 1755-60. 4.40 UR   1224

--------Herrn Georg Andreas Sorgens anleitung zum
generalbass und zur composition. Berlin, 1760.
1.60 UR   1225

--------Kritische einleitung in die geschichte und
lehrsatze der alten und neuen musik. Berlin, 1759.
2.80 UR   1226

--------Die kunst das clavier zu spielen. Berlin,
1760-61. 1.60 UR   1227

--------Legende einiger musikheiligen. Breslau,
1786. 2.80 UR   1228

--------Neue methode allerley arten von temperaturen dem claviere. Berlin, 1790. 1.00 UR   1229

--------Versuch uber die musikalische temperatur. Breslau, 1776. 2.80 UR   1230

Marr, Frances Harrison (S-B3)--Heart-life in song. 2d. ed. Richmond, Va., J.W. Randolph & English (etc.), 1883. 9-183p. 3.25 LoC   1231

Marrant, John (TOS-3)--A narrative of the Lord's wonderful dealings with John Marrant, ... Taken down from his relation ... and published by the Rev. Mr. Aldridge. 2d ed. London, printed by Gilbert & Plummer, 1785. 5.95 LoC   1232

Marryat, Frederick (P&R-2)--Narrative of the travels and adventures of Monsieur Violet, in California, Sonora, and western Texas. 3v. 5.95 each LoC   1233

Marshall (LR-E&W)--Common Pleas. 2v. (1813-16). MMP   1234

Martin, Farris James, Jr.--Nonfiction space travel literature for the public library. 1959. Thesis (M.A.), Univ. of Kentucky. 2.80 KU   1235

Martin, Horace (KC-10)--Pictorial guide to the Mammoth Cave, Kentucky ... Illus. ... by S. Wallen, Jno. Andrew, J.W. Orr, and N. Orr. New York, Stringer & Townsend (1851). 116p. 2.77 LoC   1236

Martini, Giovanni Battista--Storia della musica. Bologna, 1757-81. 13.50 UR   1237

Martius, Joh. Nic.--Unterricht von der Magia Naturali und derselben medicinischen Gebrauch. Franckfurth und Leipzig, 1724. Nr.191-194. MK   1238

Martyn, Benjamin (TOS-4)--An impartial enquiry into the state and utility of the province of Georgia. London, printed for W. Meadows, 1741. 5.95 LoC 1239

Mason, Jonathan (TOS-2)--Extracts from a diary ... of
a journey from Boston to Savannah in the year 1804.
Cambridge [Mass.] John Wilson & Son, University
Press, 1885.   5.95 LoC   1240

Massey, Sally Ross (PH-55)--A study of the stress
relationships among and within individuals with regard
to metabolic rate and cardiorespiratory change.
1957. Thesis (M. Ed.), Woman's College, Univ. of
North Carolina. 59p. 1.05 O   1241

May, John (TOS-3)--Journal and letters ... relative to
two journeys to the Ohio country in 1788 and '89. With
a biographical sketch by Rev. Richard S. Edes ...
and illustrative notes by W.M. Darlington. ...
Cincinnati, R. Clarke & Co., for the Hist. & Philosophical
Society of Ohio, 1873. 5.95 LoC   1242

May, Samuel, 1810 (AP-1)--The fugitive slave law, and
its victims. New York, American Anti-slavery Society,
1856. 48p. 2.45 LoC   1243

Mead, Charles (TOS-4)--Mississippian scenery; a poem,
descriptive of the interior of North America. Philadelphia,
pub. by S. Potter & Co., ... W. Fry, printer, 1819.
5.95 LoC   1244

Meade, William (S-B4)--Old churches, ministers and
families of Virginia ... Philadelphia, J.B. Lippincott
& Co., 1861. 2v. plates 3.95 LoC   1245

Meadows, Paul Eugene (PE-414)--The effect of isotonic
and isometric muscle contraction training on speed,
force, and strength. 1959. Thesis (Ph.D.), Univ.
of Illinois. 113p. 1.40 O   1246

Medical clinics of North America. (1959-   ). 7.00
per vol. F   1247

        Medley, Mat (pseud.)--See Aston, Anthony

Megone's Company Cases (LR-E&W)--Company. 2v.
(1888-91). MMP   1248

Meigs, Charles Delucena, 1792 (KC-14)--A biographical
notice of Daniel Drake, M.D., of Cincinnati. Prepared
by appointment of the College of Physicians of
Philadelphia. Read at the meeting, July, 1853.
Philadelphia, Lippincott, Grambo & Co., 1853.
38p. 3.95 LoC   1249

Melish, John (TOS-2)--A description of the roads in
the United States. ... Philadelphia, printed by G. Palmer,
1814. 5.95 LoC   1250

--------(TOS-2)--A geographical description of the
United States, ... Philadelphia, the author, 1816.
5.95 LoC   1251

--------(TOS-2)--Information and advice to emigrants
to the United States: ... Philadelphia, printed for and
pub. by John Melish, 1819. 5.95 LoC   1252

--------(TOS-4)--A statistical account of the United
States, ... From the census of 1810. ... Philadelphia,
printed by G. Palmer, 1813. 5.95 LoC   1253

--------(TOS-3)--The traveller's directory through the
United States. ... Philadelphia, for the author,
1815. 2v. 5.95 each LoC   1254

--------(TOS-2)--Travels through the United States of
America in the years 1806-07 and 1809-11; ...
Philadelphia, printed for the author, ... 1812. 2v.
5.95 each LoC   1255

Mellor, Enoch (AP-1)--War or slavery. Manchester,
Union & Emancipation Society, n.d. 2p. 2.45 LoC 1256

Memoires pour servier a l'histoire de la revolution operee
dans la musique par M. le Chevalier Gluck. Naples,
1781. 2.80 UR   1257

Memorial on the upward forces of fluids and their applicability
to several arts, sciences and public improvements; for
which a patent has been granted by the U.S. to the author,
Edmond Charles Genet, a citizen of the U.S. Albany,
1825. 2.00 SM   1258

Mercier, Alfred (S-B3)--Le fou de Palermo; nouvelle
siciliennek, par M. Louisianais (pseud.). Nouvelle-
Orleans, Impr. du "Carillon," 1873. 140p. 3.25
LoC   1259

--------(S-B3)--L'habitation Saint-Ybars; ou, Maitres
et esclaves en Louisiane, recit social. Nouvelle-
Orleans, Impr. Franco-Americaine (E. Antoine),
1881. 234p. 3.25 LoC   1260

--------(S-B3)--Lidia. Nouvelle-Orleans, Impr.
Franco-Americaine d'E. Antoine, 1887. 102p.
3.25 LoC   1261

Merki, Donald John (HE-51)--Relationship of health
knowledge of high school seniors to basic science
background. 1956. Thesis (M.S.), Univ. of Illinois.
82p. 1.40 O   1262

Meserve, Arthur (OV-A5)--The Indian spirit; or,
Perils of the border. A story of Indian warfare.
New York, George Munro (1868). 100p. 3.09
LoC   1263

--------(OV-A5)--The painted paleface; or, The
scourge of the river. New York, George Munro
(1868). 97p. 3.07 LoC   1264

Mesick, J. L.--English traveller in America, 1785-
1835. 3.00 SM   1265

Mesuě, Joannes, 924 or 5-1015 (HS-1)--Mesue cum
expositione mondini super canones vniuersales.
[Venetijs, Impressa per J. & G. de Gregorijs fratres,
1497] 360 (i.e. 372)l 5.58 LoC   1266

--------(HS-1)--Opus qbuslibet aromatariis: necessariu.
Mesue in uulgare rescripto. [Venice? 1500?] 33 l
Headings in Latin; text in Italian. Copinger 4011.
2.85 LoC   1267

Miall, Charles S. (AP-1)--The proposed slave empire;
its antecedents, constitution, and policy. London,
E. Stock, 1863. 32p. 2.45 LoC   1268

Michaux, Francois Andre (TOS-2)--Voyage à l'ouest
des mont Alléghanys, dans les états de l'Ohio, du
Kentucky et du Tennessée,... Paris, Levrault,
Schoell et cie., 1804. 5.95 LoC   1269

Micheli, P.A.--Nova genera plantarum, 1729. 2.2
MMe   1270

Middleton, Charles Theodore (TOS-3)--A new and
complete system of geography. ... London, printed
for J. Cooke, 1777-78. 2v. 5.95 each LoC   1271

Mifflin, Benjamin (TOS-4)--Journal ... record of a
tour from Philadelphia to Delaware and Maryland,
... 1762; ed. by V.H. Paltsits, New York, The New
York Public Library, 1935. 5.95 LoC   1272

Migne, Jacques Paul--Patrologiae cursus completus:
series Graeca. Paris, 1844-64. 161v. in 166
660.00 F   1273

--------Patrologiae cursus completus: Series Latina.
Paris, 1844-82. 221v. 850.00 F   1274

Mike Fink Miscellany. (Titles starred have appeared
in other LoC series, as noted; may be omitted if
purchaser already has LoC series or single titles)
Group price, 4.45 per vol. LoC   1275
The titles in this series are:
    *Ashe, T. (also OV-A4)--Travels in America
    Baird, R.--View of the Valley of the Mississippi
    *Bennett, E. (also OV-A1)..Mike Fink.
    Casseday, B.--History of Louisville, ...
    *Cuming, F. (also TOS-2)--Sketches of a tour to
        the western country.
    *Evans, E. (also TOS-2)--A pedestrious tour of
        4000 miles.
    Finley, J.B.--Life among the Indians.
    *Gould, E. (also KC-11)--Fifty years on the
        Mississippi.
    Haliburton, T.C., ed.--Traits of American humor.
    Hall, J.--Letters of the West.
    Hall, J.--Statistics of the West, at the close of the
        year 1836.

*Hall, J. (also OV-A2)--The West--its commerce
and navigation.
Howe, H.--The Great West.
Howe, H.--Historical collections of Ohio.
Keyes, J.--Pioneers of Scioto County.
*McClung, J.A. (also OV-A1; KC-1)--Sketches
of Western adventure.
McKnight, C.--Our Western border.
Mitford, M.R.--Lights and shadows of American
life.
Milburn, W.H.--Ten years of preacher life.
*Monette, J.W. (also OV-A3)--History of the
discovery of the valley of the Mississippi.
Musick, J.R.--Stories of Missouri.
Perrin, W.H., et. al.--Kentucky, a history of the
state.
Richardson, A.D.--Beyond the Mississippi.
Rozier, F.A.--...Early settlements of the
Mississippi Valley.
Scharf, J.T.--History of St. Louis City and County.
*Strickland, W.P., ed. (also TOS-5)--Peter
Cartwright, ...
Thorpe, T.B.--The hive of the bee-hunter
Thorpe, T.B.--Mysteries of the backwoods.
Tripplett, F.--Conquering the wilderness.
Van Buren, A. de P.--Jottings of a year's sojourn
in the South.
*Venable, W.H. (also OV-A3)--Beginnings of a
literary culture in the Ohio Valley.
*The Western Souvenir (also OV-A1).

Milburn, William Henry (OV-A5)--The rifle, axe, and
saddle-bags, and other lectures. With an introd.
by Rev. J. McClintock. New York, Derby & Jackson
(etc.), 1857. 309p. 5.39 LoC   1276

--------(MFM)--Ten years of preacher life. 1859.
363p. 5.48 LoC   1277

Military Gentleman (P&R-2)--Notes on the Missouri
River and some of the native tribes in its neighborhood.
5.95 LoC   1278

Miller, Andrew (TOS-2)--New States and territories, ...
   printed for the benefit of emigrants and others,
   intending to visit the western country. N.p., 1819.
   5.95 LoC   1279

Milligen, George (TOS-4)--A short description of the
   province of South-Carolina, ... Written ... 1763.
   London, printed for J. Hinton, 1770. 5.95 LoC   1280

Mills, Samuel John (TOS-2)--...Missionary tour through
   that part of the United States which lies west of the
   Allegany Mountains; ... Andover, Flagg & Gould,
   1815. 5.95 LoC   1281

Mitchell, John (TOS-2)--The present state of Great
   Britain and North America, ... London, printed for
   T. Becket & P.A. de Hondt, 1767. 5.95 LoC   1282

Mitchell, William M. (KC-9)--The underground railroad
   from slavery to freedom. London, 1860. 172p.
   3.88 LoC   1283

Mitford, Mary Russell (MFM)--Lights and shadows of
   American life. 1832. 3v. v1, 4.98; v2, 4.48;
   v3, 4.48   LoC   1284

Monardes, Nicolas, 1512 (ca.)- 1588 (HS-1)--Primera
   y segvnda y tercera partes de la historia medicinal
   de la cosas que se traen de nuestras Indias Occidentales
   que siruen en medicina. Sevilla, A. Escriuano,
   1574. 206p. 3.76   LoC   1285

Monette, John Wesley (MFM, also OV-A3)--History of
   the discovery of the valley of the Mississippi. 1846.
   2v. v1, 9.20; v2, 9.54   LoC   1286

Monro, Acta Cancellariae (LR-E&W)--Chancery. 1v.
   (1545-1625). MMP   1287

Montagu (LR-E&W)--Bankruptcy. 1v. (1829-32). MMP 1288

Montagu & Ayrton (LR-E&W)--Bankruptcy. 3v. (1833-
   38). MMP   1289

Montagu & Chitty (LR-E&W)--Bankruptcy. 1v. (1838-40). MMP   1290

Montagu & McArthur (LR-E&W)--Bankruptcy. 1v. (1828-29). MMP   1291

Montague & Bligh (LR-E&W)--Bankruptcy. 1v. (1832-33). MMP   1292

Montague, Deacon & De Gex (LR-E&W)--Bankruptcy. 3v. (1840-44). MMP   1293

Montéclair, Michel Pignolet de--Principes de musique. Paris, 1736. 1.50 UR   1294

Montlezun, Baron de (TOS-2)--Voyage fait dans les années 1816-17, de New-York à la Nouvelles Orleans, et de L'Orenoque au Mississippi, ... Paris, Gide Fils, 1818. 2v. 5.95 each LoC   1295

Montule, Edward de (TOS-4)--Voyage en Amérique, ... pendant les années, 1816 ... 1819. Paris, Dalaunay et Belon, 1821. 2v. 5.95 each LoC   1296

Moody, F.W.--A grammar of the dialect of Addingham in the West Riding of Yorkshire. Thesis (M.A.). 1.15 MMe   1297

Moore, Francis (TOS-4)--A voyage to Georgia; begun in the year 1735. Containing an account of the settling of the town of Frederica, ... London, printed for Jacob Robinson, 1744. 5.95 LoC   1298

Moore, George Clark (PE-393)--An analytical study of physical fitness test variables. 1955. Thesis (Ph.D.), Univ. of Illinois. 133p. 1.65 O   1299

Moore, J.B. (LR-E&W)--Common Pleas. 12v. (1817-27). MMP   1300

Moore & Payne (LR-E&W)--Common Pleas. 5v. (1827-31). MMP   1301

Moore & Scott (LR-E&W)--Common Pleas. 4v. (1831-34). MMP   1302

Moré, Charles Albert, Chevalier de Pontgibaud,
Comte de (TOS-4)--Memoires du comte de Moré
precédés de cinq lettres de considérations sur les
Memoires particuliers. Paris, Victor Thiercelin,
1827. 5.95 LoC   1303

More, Thomas--The workes of Sir Thomas More. Ed.
by William Bastell. London, 1557. 8.00 F   1304

Moreau de Saint-Mery, Mederic-Louis-Elie (TOS-3)--
Voyage aux Etats-Unis de l'Amérique, 1793-98.
Ed. with an introd. and notes by S. L. Mims. New
Haven, Yale Univ. Press, 1913. 5.95 LoC   1305

Morehead, Charles Slaughter, 1802 (AP-1)--Who commenced
the war? The following extracts from the testimony of
Gov. Morehead, of Ky., throws (!) light on this subject.
N.p., n.d. 4p. 2.45 LoC   1306

Morgan, John Hunt, 1825-1864 (AP-1)--History of Gen.
John Hunt Morgan. New York, Knapp & Co., c1888.
16p. 2.45 LoC   1307

Morland, Richard B. (PE-394)--A philosophical interpreta-
tion of the educational views held by leaders in American
physical education. 1958. Thesis (Ph.D.), New York
Univ. 540p. 3.65 O   1308

Mori, Samuel (KC-11)--Zwei briefe aus Amerika. Bern,
Buchdruckerei des "Berner boten, " 1886. 64p. 2.50
LoC   1309

Morris, Maurice O'Connor (P&R-1)--Rambles in the
Rocky Mountains: with a visit to the gold fields of
Colorado. 5.95 LoC   1310

Morton, E.J. (AP-1)--The American war, and the
conflict of principles therein involved. Halifax, T. & W.
Birtwhistle, 1863. 16p. 2.45 LoC   1311

Mowry, Hon. Sylvester (P&R-2)--The geography and
resources of Arizona and Sonora: an address before
the American Geographical & Statistical Society.
5.95 LoC   1312

Mozart, Leopold--Versuch einer grundlichen violinschule.
Augspurg, 1756. 2.40 UR   1313

Mühlenberg, Henry Melchior (TOS-1)--Heinrich Melchior
Muhlenberg, Patriarch der Luterischen Kirche Nordameri-
kas, Selbstbiographie, 1711-1743. ... Allentown, Pa.,
Brobst, Diehl & Co. (etc.), 1881. 5.95 LoC   1314

Muhlenberg, Henry Augustus, 1823 (KC-14)--The life of
Major-General Peter Muhlenberg of the Revolutionary
Army. Philadelphia, Carey & Hart, 1849. ...456p.
3.95 LoC   1315

Mullan, John (P&R-1)--Miners and travelers' guide to
Oregon, Washington, Idaho, Montana, Wyoming, and
Colorado. ... 5.95 LoC   1316

Murfree, Mary Noailles (S-B4)--In the "Stranger peoples"
country; a novel by Charles Egbert Craddock (pseud.)
... New York, Harper & Brothers, 1891. ...360p.
illus. 3.95 LoC   1317

--------(S-B3)--The mystery of Witch-Face mountain and
other stories, by Charles Egbert Craddock (pseud.).
Boston & New York, Houghton, Mifflin & Co., 1895.
279p. 3.25 LoC   1318

--------(S-B3)--The story of Keedon bluffs, by Charles
Egbert Craddock (pseud.). Boston & New York, Houghton,
Mifflin & Co., 1888. 257p. 3.25 LoC   1319

--------(S-B4)--The story of old Fort Loudon, by
Charles Egbert Craddock (pseud.) ... with illus. by
Ernest C. Peixoto. New York, Macmillan Co., 1899.
...409p. 3.95 LoC   1320

--------(S-B4)--The young mountaineers; short stories
by Charles Egbert Craddock (pseud.) with illus. by
Malcolm Fraser. Boston & New York, Houghton,
Mifflin & Co., 1897. ...262p. 3.95 LoC   1321

Murphy & Hurlstone (LR-E&W)--Exchequer. 1v. (1836-
37). MMP   1322

Murray, Charles Augustus (P&R-1)--Travels in North
America during the years 1834-36. Including a
summer residence with the Pawnee tribe of Indians,
... and a visit to Cuba and the Azore Islands. 2v.
5.95 each LoC   1323

Murray, James (TOS-4)--Letters of James Murray,
loyalist; ed. by N.M. Tiffany, assisted by S.I. Lesley.
Boston, printed; not pub., 1901. 5.95 LoC   1324

Musick, John R. (MFM)--Stories of Missouri. 1897.
288p. 4.66 LoC   1325

Mynsicht, Adrian von, 1603-1638 (HS-1)--Thesavrvs
et armamentarivm medico-chymicvm. Cui in fine
adiunctum est Testamentvm Hadrianevm de aureo
philosophorum lapide. Lvgdvni, Sumpt. I.A. Hvgvetan,
1640. 490, 68p. 4.90 LoC   1326

                          N

N., J.C. (TOS-3)--Naauwkeurige Beschryving van Noord-
America zynde thans het toneel des oorlogs, ...
Door J.C.N. Geboortig. ... Adriaan Walpot en Zoon,
Te Dodrecht, 1780. 5.95 LoC   1327

Narrangansett Club Publications Series 1, Vols. 1 to 6.
(The collected writings of Roger Williams) 25.00SM 1328

National Institute of Industrial Psychology. The measurement of manual dexterities: report no. 4. 0.10.6
MMe   1329

National Institute of Industrial Psychology. Occupation
analysis: report no. 1. 0.10.6 MMe   1330

Neilson, Peter (TOS-2)--Recollections of a six years'
residence in the United States of America. ... Glasgow,
David Robertson; Edinburgh, Wm. Tate, 1830. 5.95
LoC   1331

Nelson, Dale O. (PSY-96)--Studies of transfer of learning
in gross motor skills. 1957. Thesis (Ph.D.),
Univ. of Southern California. 170p. 1.90 O   1332

Nelson, Steve--The unpublished works in Thomas Myriell's
Tristitiae Remedium (1616). 1958. Thesis
(M.Mus.), Baylor Univ. 2.25 UR   1333

Nesom, Guy Wilburn (PE-415)--An evaluation of physical
education in public high schools of Louisiana. 1959.
Thesis (Ed.D.), George Peabody College for Teachers.
288p. 2.30 O   1334

Ness, Philip E. & Sharos, Charles L. (PE-380)--The
effect of weight training on leg strength and the vertical
jump. 1956. Thesis (M.S.), Springfield College.
65p. 1.05 O   1335

Neville & Manning (LR-E&W)--King's Bench. 6v. (1832-
36). MMP   1336

Neville & Perry (LR-E&W)--King's Bench. 3v. (1836-
38). MMP   1337

Neville & Perry (LR-E&W)--Magistrate's Cases. 1v.
(1836-37). MMP   1338

New England Journal of Medicine. (1959-   ). 7.50
per vol. F   1339

New Practice Cases (Welford, Bittleston & Parnell)
(LR-E&W)--Bail. 3v. (1844-48). MMP   1340

New Reports (LR-E&W)--All. 6v. (1862-65). MMP   1341

New Republic. Vols. 1 to 15 (Nov.7, 1914- July 27,
1918). 60.55 SM   1342

A new voyage to Georgia (TOS-3). By a young gentleman.
Giving an account of his travels to South Carolina,
and part of North Carolina. ... London, J. Wilford,
1735. 5.95 LoC   1343

"New York Law Journal." 1958 - 73.94; 1959 - 79.59;
1960 - 84.84; current subs., 21cents per side
GML   1344

Nicaise, Auguste (P&R-2)--Une annee au desert; scenes
et recits du Far-West Americain. 5.95 LoC   1345

Nichols, Mary Elizabeth (ACRL-111)--Early development
of the University of Mississippi library. 1957.
Thesis (M.L.S.), Univ. of Mississippi. .75 UR   1346

Nicolai, Ernst Anton--Die Verbindung der Musik mit
der Artzneygelahrheit. Halle, 1745. Nr.213-214.
MK   1347

Niemeyer, Roy K. (PSY-97)--Part versus whole methods
and massed versus distributed practice in the learning
of selected large muscle activities. 1958. Thesis
(Ph.D.), Univ. of Southern California. 176p. 1.90
O   1348

Nineteenth Century American Literature. The Ohio
Valley: Series A, Group 5.   Group price,
1.95 per vol. LoC   1349
The titles in this series are:

    Abdy, E.S.--Journal of a residence and tour in
        the United States ...
    Anderson, C.--Address on Anglo-Saxon destiny.
    Anderson, C.--Oration on the real nature and
        value of the American Revolution.
    Ashe, T.--Memoirs of Mammoth, ...
    Ashe, T.--Memoirs and confessions.
    Atwater, C.--General character ... of the people
        of Ohio.
    Baird, R.--View of the Valley of the Mississippi.
    Breckinridge, R.J.--Discourse on the formation
        and development of the American mind.
    Brewster, G.--Lectures on education.
    Bristed, J.--Resources of the United States ...
    Bullock, W.--Sketch of a journey through the Western
        states ...
    Buttrick, T.--Voyages, travels and discoveries.
    Campbell, J.W.--Biographical sketches; ...

Colby, J.--Life, experiences and travels ...
Cox, S.C.--Recollections of the early settlement
  of the Wabash Valley.
Delafield, J., 1812.--Inquiry into the origin of the
  antiquities of America.
Edwards, S.E.--The Ohio hunter; ...
Elemjay, L.--Letters and miscellanies ...
Elmore, J.B.--A liver in Cuba, and poems.
Emmons, R.--The Fredoniad; ...
Emmons, R.--The battle of Bunker Hill, ...
Emmons, R.--The national jubilee, ...
Eyre, J.--Travels:...
Finley, J.B.--Autobiography.
Finley, J.B.--History of the Wyandott mission, ...
Flint, T.--Oration, ...
Flint, T.--Life and adventures of Arthur Glenning ...
Flint, T.--Francis Berrian, ...
Garrett, L.--Recollections of the West.
Genin, T.H.--The Napolead.
Grund, F.J.--Aristocracy in America.
Guest, M.--Poems on several occasions.
Hall, F.--Letters from the East and from the West.
Hibernicus; or Memoirs of an Irishman, ...
Hawley, Z.--Journal of a tour ...
James, U.P.--The Negro melodist: ...
Jones, C.A.--The outlaw, and other poems.
Meserve, A.--The Indian spirit; ...
Meserve, A.--The painted paleface; ...
Milburn, W.H.--The rifle, axe, and saddle-bags, ...
Owen, R.D.--Labor: its history and its prospects.
Owen, R.D.--The wrong of slavery, ...
Owen, R.D.--...Autobiography.
Paxton, J.D.--Letters on slavery; ...
Peers, B.O.--American education; ...
Reid, J.S.--Gulzar; ...
Say, T.--American conchology; ...
Say, T.--American entomology:...
Smith, H.M.--At midnight and other poems.
Smith, J.--Poems ...
Spencer, O.M.-- Indian captivity; ...
Stein, E.--One way to the woods.
Stiles, J.C.--Modern reform examined; ...
Thomas, F.W.--Autobiography ...
Thomas, F.W.--The beechen tree.
Thomas, F.W.--Clinton Bradshaw; ...

Thomas, F.W.--The emigrant; ...
Umphraville, A.--The siege of Baltimore, ...
Wakefield, J.A.--...War between the United States
    and the Sac and Fox Nations of Indians, ...
Walker, T.--Annual discourse, ...
Ward,J.W.--The song of higher water.
Whiting, H.--Ontwa, the son of the forest.
Whiting, H.--Sanillac, a poem.
Wilstach, J.A.--The battle forest; a poem.
Wislizenus, A.--Ein ausflug nach den Felsen-
    gebirgen ...
Woods, J.--Shakerism unmasked; ...
Wylie, A.--Address ...

Nineteenth Century American Literature. The South:
    Series B, Group 3. Group price, 1.95 per vol.
    LoC   1350
    The titles in this series are:

    Barbe, W.--In the Virginias, ...
    Boner, J.H.--Whispering pines.
    Canonge, L.--Maudit passeport!
    Cardozo, J.N.--Reminiscences of Charleston.
    Chase, L.B.--English serfdom and American
        slavery; ...
    Chesnutt, C.W.--The conjure woman.
    Cocke, Z.--A Doric reed.
    Crim, Miss M.--The Heathercotes.
    Crozier, R.H.--Hal Gilamn; ...
    Debouchel, V.--Histoire de la Louisiane; ...
    De la Houssaye, Mme. S.--Pouponne et Balthazar, ...
    De Leon, T.C.--Crag-nest.
    Dozier, C.T.--Foibles of fancy and rhymes of the
        times.
    Dugger, S.M.--The balsam groves of the Grandfather
        Mountain: ...
    Dugué, C.O.--Mila; ...
    Dumas, W.T.--The dinner horn.
    Duval, J.C.--The adventures of Big-foot Wallace, ...
    Elliott, S.B.--A simple heart.
    Gordon, A.C.--Befo' de war; ...
    Harben, W.M.--White Marie; ...
    Herrington, W.D.--The deserter's daughter.
    Hope, J.B.--Arms and the man: ...
    Hope, J.B.--A collection of poems.

Hope, J.B.--An elegiac ode: ...
Hope, J.B.--A poem: ...
Hope, J.B.--A wreath of Virginia bay leaves .
Ingraham, J.H.--Bonfield: ...
Ingraham, J.H.--Forrestal: ...
Ingraham, J.H.--The silver ship of Mexico.
Ingraham, J.H.--The Odd fellow, ...
Ingraham, J.H.--The Spectre Steamer, ...
Ingraham, J.H.--Wildash; ...
Ingraham, J.H.--The wing of the wind.
Jones, J.B.--Adventures of Col Gracchus Vanderbomb,
Jones, J.B.--The rival belles; ...
Johnston, R.M.--Old times in middle Georgia.
Kennedy, J.P.--The border states, ...
Kennedy, J.P.--Mr. Ambrose's letters on the
  rebellion.
Legare, J.M.--Orta-undis, and other poems.
McCabe, J.D.--The aid-de-camp.
McCabe, J.D.--The life of Thomas J. Jackson.
Marks, E.--Elfreide of Guldal, a Scandinavian legend.
Marr, F.H.--Heart-life in song.
Mercier, A.--Le fou de Palermo; ...
Mercier, A.--L'habitation Saint-Ybars; ...
Mercier, A.--Lidia.
Murfree, M.N.--The mystery of Witch-Face
  mountain ...
Murfree, M.N.--The story of Keedon bluffs ...
Peck, W.H.--The Confederate flag on the ocean.
Peck, W.H.--The fortune-teller of New Orleans; ...
Peck, W.H.--The M'Donalds; ...
Pendleton, L.B.--Corona of the Nantahalas.
Pendleton, L.B.--In the Okefenokee; ...
Preston, W.C.--Eulogy on Hugh Swinton Legare; ...
Reese, L.W.--A branch of May.
Robinson, J.H.--The Lone Star; ...
Robinson, J.H.--Marion's Brigade; ...
Robinson, J.H.--Milrose; ...
Robinson, J.H.--The White Rover; ...
Ruffin, E.--African colonization unveiled.
Ruffin, E.--The political (!) [sic] economy of slavery;
Simms, W.G.--Areytos; ...
Simms, W.G.--Atlantis.
Simms, W.G.--The golden Christmas.
Slaughter, P.--History of Bristol Parish, Va.
Slaughter, P.--History of St. Mark's Parish, Va.

Smith, W.R.--The Royal Ape: a dramatic poem.
Stockard, H.J.--Fugitive lines.
Testut, C.--Le vieux Salomon; ...
Thompson, M.--A fortnight of folly.
Thompson, M.--Lincoln's grave.
Tiernan, Mrs. F.C.--"The land of the sky;" ...
Tucker, N.B.--Prescience. ...
Tucker, S.G.--Reflections on the cession of
    Louisiana to the United States.
Weeden, Miss H.--Bandanna ballads, ...

Nineteenth Century American Literature. The South:
  Series B, Group 4. Group price, 1.95 per vol.
  LoC   1351
The titles in this series are:
    Alexander, J.W.--Forty years' familiar letters ...
    Altsheler, J.A.--A herald of the West; ...
    Altsheler, J.A.--A soldier of Manhattan, ...
    Altsheler, J.A.--The sun of Saratoga,   ...
    Baskett, J.N.--"At you'all's house;"
    Barbe, W.--Ashes and incense, poems.
    Bayne, C.J.--The water-spirit's bride and other
       poems.
    Boyle, Mrs. V--The other side, an historic poem.
    Brown, J.H.--History of Texas, from 1685 to 1892.
    Camp, G.K.--Shadows.
    Caruthers, W.A.--A lecture delivered ... at the
       Unitarian Church, ...
    Chestnutt, C.W.--The wife of his youth, ...
    Claiborne, J.F.H.--Life and correspondence of
       John A. Quitman, ...
    Claiborne, J.F.H.--Mississippi, ...
    Cotton stealing. A novel.
    Dabney, R.L.--The new South.
    Dabney, R.L.--A defense of Virginia, ...
    Dandridge, Mrs. D.--Rose Brake; poems.
    Davis, Mrs. M.E.--In war times at La Rose Blanche.
    Davis, Mrs. M.E.--Under the man-fig.
    Davis, Mrs. M.E.--The wire cutters.
    De Leon, T.C.--Joseph Wheeler, ...
    De Leon, T.C.--The pride of the Mercers.
    De Leon, T.C.--The reding of the solid South; ...
    De Leon, T.C.--South songs; ...
    Derby, J.C.--Fifty years among authors, books and
       publishers.

Dixon, S.H.--The poets and poetry of Texas.
Dorsey, Mrs. S.A.--Panola.
Edwards, H.S.--The Marbeau cousins.
Edwards, H.S.--Two runaways, ...
Eggleston, G.C.--A rebel's recollections.
Elliott, E.N., ed.--Cotton is king, ...
Fagan, W.L.--Southern war songs.
Fitzgerald, O.P.--California sketches.
Fitzgerald, O.P.--Judge Longstreet.
Folsom, M.M.--Scraps of song and Southern scenes...
Foote, H.S.--Address ...
Fortier, A.--Louisiana sketches.
Garrett, P.F.--The authentic life of Billy, the kid, ...
Garrett, W.--Reminiscences of public men in
    Alabama, ...
Goulding, F.R.--The young marooners on the Florida
    coast; ...
Graves, J.T.--"The reign of the demagogue."
Hope, J.B.--Under the empire; ...
Hubner, C.W.--Poems and essays.
Hubner, C.W.--Wild flowers. Poems.
Hundley, D.R.--Social relations in our southern
    states.
Ingle, E.--Southern sidelights; ...
Ingraham, J.H.--Life and adventures of Percival
    Mayberry; ...
Ingraham, P.--Land of legendary lore; ...
Johnston, R.M.--Pearce Amerson's will ...
Johnston, R.M.--Mr. Absalom Billingslea, ...
Johnston, R.M.--The Primes and their neighbors: ...
Jones, C.C.--Memorial history of Augusta, Georgia.
Jones, C.C.--Negro myths from the Georgia coast...
Jones, J.B.--Border war; ...
Jones, J.B.--A rebel war clerk's diary ...
Jones, J.B.--Rural sports; ...
Kemble, F.A.--Journal of a residence on a Georgian
    plantation ...
Kendall, G.W.--The war between the United States
    and Mexico ...
Kennedy, W.--Texas: ...
Lucas, D.B.--The wreath of Eglantine, and other
    poems.
McCabe, W.G.--The defence of Petersburg.
Meade, W.--Old churches, ministers, and families
    of Virginia.

Murfree, M.N. --In the "Stranger people's" country.
Murfree, M.N. --The story of old Fort Loudon.
Murfree, M.N. --The young mountaineers.
Pendleton, L.B. --The sons of Ham.
Pollard, E.A. --Echoes from the South.
Pollard, E.A. --Letters of the southern spy, ...
Pollard, E.A. --The lost cause regained.
Pollard, E.A. --The southern spy; ...
Porter, D. --Poems.
The pro-slavery argument; ...
Read, O.P. --The carpetbagger.
Read, O.P. --A Tennessee judge.
Reese, L.W. --A quiet road.
Robinson, J.H. --The house of silence.
Rowland, K.M. --Life of Charles Carroll of Carrollton,
Simms, W.G. --As good as a comedy.
Simms, W.G. --The city of the silent; ...
Simms, W.G. --The geography of South Carolina: ...
Simms, W.G. --History of South Carolina ...
Simms, W.G. --The lily and the totem; ...
Simms, W.G. --Sack and destruction of the city of
    Columbia, S.C.
Simms, W.G. --South Carolina in the Revolutionary
    War; ...
Smith, F.H. --A day at Laguerre's ...
Smith, F.H. --A gentleman vagabond and some others.
Smith, W.R. --The chief. A poem ...
Smith, W.R. --Reminiscences of a long life; ...
Smithwick, N. --The evolution of a state; ...
Stillman, A.R. --How they kept the faith, ...
Thompson, M. --The king of Honey Island.
Thompson, M. --A Tallahassee girl.
Waddel, J.N. --Memorials of academic life; ...
Wilmer, R.H. --The recent past from a Southern
    standpoint.
Yoakum, H.K. --History of Texas ...

Nineteenth Century American Pamphlets. Group 1.
    143.55   LoC   1352
    The titles in this series are:

    Abraham Africanus I--His secret life, ...
    Adams, W.E. --The slaveholders' war: ...
    An American, pseud. --Letter on American slavery.
    American Civil War. Correspondence with Mr. H.C.
        Carey, ...

143

Arnold, G.--Life and adventures of Jeff Davis.
Arthur, W.--English opinion on the American
 rebellion.
Baird, H.C., 1825--George Washington and Gen.
 Jackson, ...
Barry, J., 1828?--Annals of Harper's Ferry, ...
Blodget, L., 1823--Commercial and financial strength
 of the United States, ...
Breckinridge, J.C.--History of Gen. J.C. Breckinridge.
Breckinridge, J.C.--Response of Gen. J.C.
 Breckinridge ...
Brown, G.--The American war and slavery.
Brown, J., 1800, defendant--Life, trial and convic-
 tion ...
Brown, J.M., 1851--The mountain campaigns in
 Georgia; ...
Cairnes, J.E., 1823--The revolution in America.
Canavella, C.A.--Confederate diary of C.A. Canavella,
Campbell, L.D., 1811--Speech ... on southern
 aggression, ...
Chase, P.S.--Reunion greeting, ...
Confederate States of America. District Courts.
 South Carolina--The sequestration cases, ...
Cobbe, F.P., 1822--The red flag in John Bull's eyes.
Cobden, R., 1804--Speech ... on the "Foreign
 enlistment act," ...
Crosby, A., 1810--Present position of the seceded
 states, ...
[Davis, J.]--In memoriam. Jefferson Davis.
Day, T.C.--The Democratic Party as it was and
 as it is!
Dill, R.--The American conflict; ...
Dudley, W.W., 1842--The Iron Brigade at Gettysburg.
Dunkle, J.J.--Prison life during the rebellion.
Earl Russell and the slave power.
Elder, W., 1806--Debt and resources of the United
 States: ...
English, W.H., 1822--The Kansas question.
English neutrality. Is the Alabama a British pirate?
Escape of Gen. John H. Morgan and Capt. Thos. H.
 Hines from the Ohio penitentiary, ...
Estcourt, J.H.--Rebellion and recognition.
Everett, E., 1794--The great issues now before the
 country.
Ewing, T., 1789--Letter ... to his excellency
 Benj. Stanton, ...

Fallacies of freemen and foes of liberty.

Fifth annual reunion of the 1st Kentucky Orphan Brigade, C.S.A.

Forman, B.R.--The Confederate prisoners in northern prisons during the war.

Fredericksburg and Adjacent National Battlefields Memorial Park Assoc.

Garnett, M.R.H., 1821--The Union, past and future; ...

Gordon, J.B., 1832--The old south.

Gow, D.--Civil War in America; ...

Hall, N., 1816--The American war.

Hall, N., 1816--The pro-slavery religion of the south.

Hill, D.H., 1859--The old south.

Hodge, G.B., 1828--Sketch of the 1st Kentucky Brigade, ...

Holt, J., 1807--Speech ...

Hood, J.B.--History of Gen. J.B. Hood.

Hughes, T., 1822--The cause of Freedom: ...

James, F.B.--McCook's brigade at the assault upon Kenesaw Mountain, ...

Jay, J., 1817--The Great Issue.

Johnston, A.S.--History of Gen. A.S. Johnston.

Johnston, W., 1804--Address ...

Kelley, W.D., 1814--Addresses ...

Kelley, W.D.--The South--its resources and wants.

Kentucky. Commissioners to the Peace Conference at Washington, ...

King, A.--British sympathy in the American crisis.

L., E.--Notes on American affairs.

Laboulaye, E.R., 1811--Why the North cannot consent to disunion.

Leatham, E.A.--Speech ... upon American affairs.

Leland, C.G., 1824--Ye book of copperheads.

Leng, W.C.--The American war: ...

Long, A., 1816--Speech ...

May, S., 1810--The fugitive slave law, and its victims.

Mellor, E.--War or slavery.

Miall, C.S.--The proposed slave empire; ...

Morehead, C.S., 1802--Who commenced the war?

Morgan, J.H.--History of Gen. J.H. Morgan.

Morton, E.J.--The American war, ...

Opinions of the liberal press on the correspondence between Mr. Cobden, M.P., and Mr. Delane, the editor of the "Times."

Owen, R.D.--The future of the Northwest: ...
Owen, R.D., 1801--The policy of emancipation.
Patton, W.W., 1821--Correspondence ...
Patton, W.W., 1821--Slavery and infidelity, ...
Perry, J.J., 1811--Freedom national--slavery
    sectional.
Pierrepont, E., 1817--A review ... of Gen. Butler's
    defense, ...
Report of the judge advocate general on "The Order
    of American Knights," alias "The Sons of Liberty."
Robb, J., 1814--A southern confederacy.
Rosecrans, W.S., 1819--Letters ...
Rouse, J.--Horrible massacre at Guyandotte, Va., ...
Shea, G., 1826--Jefferson Davis: ...
Smith, E.K.--History of Gen. E.K. Smith.
Smith, G., 1823--England and America.
Speed, J.F., 1814--Reminiscences of Abraham
    Lincoln ...
Spence, J., 1816--On the recognition of the Southern
    Confederation.
Stephens, A.H.--Secession condemned in a southern
    convention.
Stille, C.J., 1819--How a free people conduct a
    long war: ...
Stoddard, A.F.--Slavery or Freedom in America, ...
Stowe, Mrs. H.E., 1811--A reply, ...
Sumner, C., 1811--Our foreign relations.
Sumner, C., 1811--Speech ...
Taylor, W., 1821--Cause and probable results of the
    Civil War in America.
Townsend, J.--The southern states, ...
U.S. Army--Report of Lt. Gen. U.S. Grant ...
War ships for the southern Confederacy: ...
Whipple, C.K.--The family relation, as affected by
    slavery.
White, R.G., 1821--The new gospel of peace, ...
Worthington, T., 1807--...History of the Battle of
    Shiloh, ...
Young, L.D., 1842--Reminiscences of a soldier of
    the Orphan Brigade.

Noel, Theophilus (P&R-1, also CT)--A campaign from
    Santa Fe to the Mississippi; being a history of the old
    Sibley Brigade ... in the years 1861-64. 5.95 LoC 1353

Nolte, Vincent Otto (TOS-3)--Fifty years in both hemispheres; ... Trans. from the German. ... New York,
Redfield, 1854. 5.95 LoC   1354

Nordhoff, C.--The communistic societies of the U.S.
3.50 SM   1355

Nordlinger, John H. (RC-32)--A study to determine how
completely the summer playground program is meeting
the recreational needs of the school children of Chelsea,
Michigan. 1958. Thesis (M.A.), Univ. of Michigan.
60p. 1.05 O   1356

The North-American and the West-Indian gazetteer
(TOS-2). Containing an authentic description of the
colonies and islands ... London, G. Robinson, 1776.
5.95 LoC   1357

North Carolina University. Studies in philology. Vols.
1-18 (1906-1923). 5.50 per vol. C   1358

Norton, John Nicholas, 1820 (KC-14)--Life of Bishop
Ravenscroft. New York, General Protestant Episcopal
Sunday School Union, and Church Book Society, 1858.
...152p. 3.95 LoC   1359

Notes and Queries. Series 1-4 (1849-73). proposed,
195.00   F   1360

Notes of Cases (ed. Thornton) (LR-E&W)--Ecclesiastical
and Maritime. 7v. (1841-59). MMP   1361

Nouvelle relation de la Caroline (TOS-3), par un gentil-
homme francois arrive, depuis deux mois, de ce
nouveau pais. ... A la Haye, Chez Meyndert Uytweff
[!] marchand libraire de meurant dans le Gorstraet
[1686?]   5.95 LoC   1362

Nuclear Science Abstracts. Vols. 1-10 (1948-1956).
in prep C   1363

    Nuttall, P. Austin--See Fuller, Thomas

Nuttall, Thomas (P&R-1, also TOS-3)--A journal of travels
into the Arkansas Territory, during the year 1819.
Philadelphia, Thomas W. Palmer, 1821. Illus. 5.95
LoC   1364

O

"Oakly"--See Holmes, Reuben

O'Brien, Donald Edward (PSY-117)--The relation between
reaction time and the type and complexity of the
succeeding task. 1959. Thesis (M.S.), Pennsylvania
State Univ. 93p. 1.40 O   1365

O'Brien, Ethel Mary (HE-42)--An investigation of persons
engaged in health education in selected high schools
in Oregon with emphasis on status, functions, qualifica-
tions and affiliations. 1959. Thesis (Ed.D.), Univ.
of Oregon. 195p. 1.75 O   1366

O'Connor, Teresa M.--The more immediate effects of
the American Revolution on Ireland. Thesis (M.A.).
2.10.6 MMe   1367

Oehler, Andrew (TOS-3)--The life, adventures and
unparalleled sufferings ... Written by himself.
Trenton, N.J., the author, 1811. 5.95 LoC   1368

Ogden, George W. (TOS-2)--Letters from the west;...
New-Bedford [Mass.] Melcher & Rogers, 1823.
5.95 LoC   1369

Ogden, Peter Skene (P&R-2)--Traits of American-Indian
life and character. By a fur trader. 5.95 LoC   1370

Olin, Stephen (TOS-2)--Life and letters ... New York,
Harper & Brothers, 1853. 2v. 5.95 each LoC   1371

The operations of the French fleet under the Count de
Grasse in 1781-2 (TOS-4), as described in two con-
temporaneous journals. [Ed. by J.D.G. Shea] New
York, 1864. 5.95 LoC   1372

Opinions of the liberal press on the correspondence
between Mr. Cobden, M.P., and Mr. Delane, the
editor of the "Times." (AP-1) Manchester, A.
Ireland & Co., 1864. 54p. 2.45 LoC   1373

Orban, William Andrew Robert (PSY-100)--An item
analysis of temperament and behavior ratings of young
boys. 1954. Thesis (M.S.), Univ. of Illinois.
61p. 1.15 O   1374

Ord, George, 1781 (KC-14)--Sketch of the life of
Alexander Wilson, author of the American ornithology.
Philadelphia, H.Hall, 1828. ...cxcixp. 3.95 LoC 1375

Ordentliche wochentliche Postzeitungen 1629 Nr. 52,
herausgegeben von Theobald Schönwetter (Stadtbibliothek
Frankfurt am Main). Nr. 185. MK   1376

Orr, Adriana Pannevis (ACRL-125)--A history and analysis
of the freshman library instruction program presented
at the University of North Carolina. 1958. Thesis
(M.S. in L.S.), Univ. of North Carolina. 1.50 UR 1377

Osborn--A study and contrast of the Kentucky mountaineer
and the bluegrass aristocrat in the works of John Fox,
Jr. 1.40 KU   1378

Osborn, Charles (TOS-3)--Journal ... Cincinnati, printed
by A. Pugh, 1854. 5.95 LoC   1379

Osgood, E.S.--The day of the cattlemen. 2.75 SM   1380

Ottman, Sidney Roger (HE-56)--Factors affecting school
lunch programs in California high schools. 1956.
Thesis (Ed.D.), Stanford Univ. 187p. 1.90 O   1381

Owen, David Dale (P&R-1)--Report of a geological
survey of Wisconsin, Iowa, and Minnesota; ...
5.95 LoC   1382

Owen, Robert Dale (AP-1)--The future of the Northwest;
in connection with the scheme of reconstruction without
New England. Philadelphia, Crissy & Markley, printers,
1863. Cover-title. 15p. 2.45 LoC   1383

149

--------(OV-A5)--Labor: its history and its prospects.
An address before the Young Men's Mercantile Library
Association of Cincinnati on Tuesday, Feb. 1, 1848.
Cincinnati, Herald of Truth Print, 1848. 39p. 2.50
LoC   1384

--------(AP-1)--The policy of emancipation: in three
letters. Philadelphia, J.B. Lippincott, 1863. 48p.
2.45 LoC   1385

--------(OV-A5)--Twenty-seven years of autobiography.
Threading my way. New York, G.W. Carleton & Co.
(etc. etc.), 1874. 360p. 5.95 LoC   1386

--------(OV-A5)--The wrong of slavery, the right of
emancipation, and the future of the African race in the
United States. Philadelphia, J.B. Lippincott & Co.,
1864. 246p. 4.70 LoC   1387

P

Packard, Alpheus Spring, 1839 (KC-12)--The Mammoth
    Cave and its inhabitants, or Descriptions of the fishes,
    insects and crustaceans found in the cave. By A.S.
    Packard, Jr. and F.W. Putnam. Salem (Mass),
    Naturalists' Agency, 1872. 62p. 2.50 LoC   1388

Page, Carl G. (TOS-3)--Darstellung der bürgerlichen
    Verhältnisse in den Freistaaten von Nord-Amerika;...
    Bautzen, Johann Gottlieb Lehmann, n.d. [183-?]
    5.95 LoC   1389

Pagès, Pierre Marie Francois, Vicomte de (TOS-2)--
    Voyages autour du monde, et vers les deux poles,
    par terre et par mer, pendant les annees 1767, ...
    1776. ...Paris, Moutard, 1782. 2v. 5.95 each
    LoC   1390

Paine, Robert (TOS-1)--Life and times of William
    M'Kendree, ... Nashville, Southern Methodist Pub.
    House, 1869. 2v. 5.95 each LoC   1391

Palairet, Jean (TOS-3)--A concise description of the
  English and French possessions in North America,
  ... London, printed by J. Haberkorn, ... 1755. 5.95
  LoC   1392

Palisot de Beauvois, Ambroise Marie Francois Joseph
  (TOS-1)--Insectes recuellis en Afrique et en Amerique,
  ...Paris, Fain & Co., printer; author and Levrault,
  Schoell et Cie, ... 1805 (1805-1821). 5.95 LoC   1393

Palliser, John (P&R-1)--Solitary rambles and adventures
  of a hunter in the prairies. 5.95 LoC   1394

Palmer, Joel (P&R-2)--Journal of travels over the Rocky
  Mountains, ... during the years 1845-46. 5.95
  LoC   1395

Palmer, John, of Lynn, Eng. (TOS-2)--Journal of travels
  in the United States of America, ... London, Sherwood,
  Neely & Jones, 1818. 5.95 LoC   1396

Palmer, John McAuley, 1817 (KC-14)--Personal recollec-
  tions of John M. Palmer; the story of an earnest life.
  Cincinnati, R. Clarke Co., 1901. ...631p. 3.95
  LoC   1397

Palmer, Lawrence Lee (PE-416)--A study of athletic
  insurance plans. 1955. Thesis (M.S.), Univ. of
  Utah. 67p. 1.15 O   1398

Parcelsus, 1493-1541 (HS-1)--Archidoxa Philippi
  Theophrastic Paracelsi Bombast ... von heymligkeyten
  der Natur zehen Bücher. Strassburg, Getruckt durch
  T. Rihel [Colophon: 1570] 484p. 6.81 LoC   1399

Parker, Agnes (KC-14)--The real Madeleine Pollard.
  A Diary of ten weeks' association with the plaintiff
  in the famous Breckinridge-Pollard suit. An intimate
  study of character. New York, G.W. Dillingham,
  1894. ...336p. 3.95 LoC   1400

Parker, Samuel (P&R-1)--Rocky Mountain Indians.
  Letter from Mr. Parker, Green River, Aug. 17, 1835.
  5.95 LoC   1401

The Parker Society. Vol. 1-55 (1841-55). 398.00;
single vols., 9.00 each LoC   1402

Parran, Antoine--Traite de la mvsiqve theoriqve et
pratiqve. Paris, 1646. 2.25 UR   1403

Pasquali, Nicolo--The art of fingering the harpsichord.
Edinburgh [1760?] 1.50 UR   1404

Pattie, James Ohio (P&R-2)--Personal narrative ...
during an expedition from St. Louis, through the vast
regions between that place and the Pacific Ocean, ...
various conflicts with the Indians, and were made
captives, ... Ed. by Timothy Flint. 5.95 LoC   1405

Pattinson, Dorothy H.--The reception of the American
constitution in Britain, 1787-1848. Thesis (M.A.).
0.15 MMe   1406

Patton, William Weston, 1821 (AP-1)--Correspondence
between W.W. Patton and the secretaries of the
Evangelical alliance on the American war. New Haven,
Conn., The New Englander, 1863. 2.45 LoC   1407

--------(AP-1)--Slavery and infidelity, or, Slavery in
the church ensures infidelity in the world. Cincinnati,
Am. Reform Book & Tract Soc., 1856. 70p. 2.45
LoC   1408

Paxton, John D. (OV-A5)--Letters on slavery; addressed
to the Cumberland congregation, Va. ... Lexington,
Ky., A.T. Skillman, 1833. 207p. 4.27 LoC   1409

        Peabody Institute, Baltimore. Library. Catalogue--
        See Catalogue of the Peabody Institute

Pearse, James (TOS-2)--A narrative of the life of James
Pearse, ... Written by himself. Rutland [Vt.] printed
by Wm. Fay for the author, 1825. 5.95 LoC   1410

Pease, T.C.--The leveller movement. 2.50 SM   1411

Peck, William Henry (S-B3)--The Confederate flag on the
    ocean. A tale of the cruises of the Sumter and the
    Alabama. New York, Van Evrie, Horton & Co., 1868.
    96p. 3.25 LoC   1412

--------(S-B3)--The fortune-teller of New Orleans; or,
    The two lost daughters. New York, Street & Smith,
    1889. 215p. 3.25 LoC   1413

--------(S-B3)--The M'Donalds; or, The ashes of southern
    homes. A tale of Sherman's march. New York,
    Metropolitan Record Office, 1867. 192p. 3.25 LoC 1414

Peckwell (LR-E&W)--Election. 2v. (1802-06). MMP 1415

Peers, Benjamin Orrs (OV-A5)--American education; or,
    Strictures on the nature, necessity, and practicability
    of a system of national education, suited to the United
    States ... New-York, J.S. Taylor, 1838. 364p.
    5.99 LoC   1416

Peirce, Bradford Kinney, 1819 (KC-14)--Life in the woods;
    or, The adventures of Audubon. Eight illus. New
    York, Carleton & Porter (c1863). 252p. 3.95 LoC 1417

Peña y Reyes, Juan Antonio de la (TOS-1)--Derrotero
    de la expedicion en la provincia de los Texas, nuevo
    reyno de Philipinas que passar a executar el muy ill.
    ... Mexico, Juan Francisco de Ortega Bonilla, 1722.
    5.95 LoC   1418

Pendleton, Louis Beauregard (S-B3)--Corona of the
    Nantahalas, a romance. New York, The Merriam Co.
    (c1895). 199p. 3.25 LoC   1419

--------(S-B3)--In the Okefenokee; a story of war time
    and the great Georgia swamp. Boston, Roberts
    Brothers, 1895. 182p. 3.25 LoC   1420

--------(S-B4)--The sons of Ham. A tale of the new South.
    Boston, Roberts Brothers, 1895. ...328p. 3.95
    LoC   1421

Penicaut, Jean (TOS-1)--Relation ou annales veritables
de ce qui s'est passe dans le pays de la Louisiane ...
avec l'histoire d'un capitaine francois et de la fille
d'un capitaine de cavalerie espagnole du Mexique.
[1699-1721] (Not printed as a separate vol.) 5.95
LoC   1422

Perrin, W.H., et al. (MFM)--Kentucky, a history of
the state. 8th ed., 1888. 930p. 12.72 LoC   1423

Perry, John Jasiel, 1811 (AP-1)--Freedom national--
slavery sectional. Washington, Buell & Blanchard,
printers, 1856. 15p. 2.45 LoC   1424

Perry & Davison (LR-E&W)--King's Bench. 4v. (1838-
41). MMP   1425

Perry's Insolvency (LR-E&W)--Bankruptcy. 1v. (1831).
MMP   1426

Perspectives in Biology and Medicine. (1959-   ).
3.00 per vol.   F   1427

Petersen, Kay Holm (PE-395)--Contrast of maturity,
structural, and strength measures between non-
participants and athletic groups of boys ten to
fifteen years of age. 1959. Thesis (Ph.D.), Univ.
of Oregon. 174p. 1.90   O   1428

Peterson, Louis John (HE-52)--The functions of departments offering doctoral preparation in school health
education. 1956. Thesis (Ed.D.), Stanford Univ.
192p. 1.90   O   1429

Peucer, M. Dan.--Lutheri merckwürdige Ausspruche
von der Buchdruckerey und den Buchdruckern.
(Leipzig, C.F. Geszner, 1743), 1740. Nr.501. MK 1430

Philips' Election Cases (LR-E&W)--Election. 1v.
(1780-81). MMP   1431

Phillimore's Judgements (LR-E&W)--Ecclesiastical.
1v. (1867-75). MMP   1432

Phipps, Maurice J. (HE-43)--Some factors influencing what children know about human growth. 1950. Thesis (M.S.), Univ. of Oregon. 47p. 1.05 O   1433

Physikalische Zeitschrift. Vols. 1-43 (1900-42). 234.50 MXT   1434

Physiological Zoology. Vols. 7-14. in prep C   1435

Pickering, Joseph (TOS-4)--Emigration, or no emigration; ... London, Longman, ... 1830. 5.95 LoC   1436

Pierrepont, Edwards, 1817 (AP-1)--A review of Judge Pierrepont of Gen. Butler's defense, before the House of Representatives, in relation to the New Orleans gold. New York, W.C. Bryant & Co., printers, 1865. 27p. 2.45 LoC   1437

Pigott & Rodwell (LR-E&W)--Registration. 1v. (1843-45). MMP   1438

Pike, Albert (P&R-1, also SB-1)--Prose sketches and poems, written in the western country. 5.95 LoC   1439

Pike, J.S.--First blows of the Civil War. 4.00 SM   1440

Pike, Zebulon Montgomery (P&R-1)--An account of expeditions to the sources of the Mississippi, and through the western parts of Louisiana, ... performed by order of the Govt. of the United States during the years 1805-07. ... 5.95 LoC   1441

Pinckney, Mrs. Eliza (Lucas) (TOS-1)--Journal and letters of Eliza Lucas. Now first printed. [Ed. by Mrs. Harriett Pinckney Holbrook] Wormsloe [Ga.] Privately printed, 1850. 5.95 LoC   1442

Placita Anglo-Normanica (LR-E&W). 1v. (1066-1195). MMP   1443

The Plains and the Rockies. Group 1 (Titles starred have
appeared in other LoC series, as noted; may be
omitted if purchaser already has LoC series or single
titles). Per vol., as a group, 4.00 (101v.) LoC   1444
The titles in this series are:

    Allen, Miss A.J.--Ten years in Oregon.
    *Bennett, E. (also OV-A1)--Forest and prairie.
    *Bennett, E. (also OV-A4)--Leni-Leoti.
    *Bennett, E. (also OV-A1)--Wild scenes on the
      frontiers.
    Berkeley, Hon. G.C.G.F.--The English sportsman
      in the western prairies.
    Bigelow, J.--Memoir of ... John Charles Fremont.
    Bliss, E.--Brief history of the new gold regions of
      Colorado ...
    Bowles, S.--Across the continent: ...
    Boynton, C.B. & T.B. Mason--Journey through
      Kansas; ...
    *Brackenridge, H.M. (also OV-A2; TOS-1)--Views
      of Louisiana; ...
    *Bradbury, J. (also TOS-1)--Travels in the interior
      of America, ...
    Bryant, E.--What I saw in California; ...
    Burton, R.F.--The City of the Saints ...
    Chandless, W.--A visit to Salt Lake; ...
    Coke, H.J.--A ride over the Rocky Mountains to
      Oregon ...
    Colt, Mrs. M.D.--Went to Kansas; ...
    *Cutler, J. (also OV-A4; TOS-1)--Topographical
      description of the State of Ohio, Indiana Territory,
      and Louisiana.
    Davis, W.W.H.--El Gringo; or New Mexico and her
      people.
    Dawson, S.J.--...Exploration of the country
      between Lake Superior and the Red River Settlement,
    Delano, A.--Life on the plains ...
    Dragoon Expedition, 1839.--Dragoon Expedition.
    Drake, S.A.--Hints and information for the use of
      emigrants to Pike's Peak, ...
    Edwards, F.S.--Campaign in New Mexico with
      Col. Doniphan.
    Edwards, P.L.--Rocky Mountain correspondence, ...
    Emory, W.H., et al.--Notes of a military reconnais-
      sance, ...

Falconer, T. --Expedition to Santa Fe.
Fisk, J. L. --Expedition to the Rocky Mountains.
Folsom, G. F. --Mexico in 1842; ...
Fox, J.W. --General courses and distance from
   G.S.L. City to Fort Limhi ...
Frobel, J. --Aus Amerika.
Gass, P. --Journal of the voyages and travels of
   a corps of discovery, ...
Gilpin, W. --The central gold region.
Goode, W.H. --Outposts of Zion, ...
Greeley, H. --Overland journey from New York to
   San Francisco, ...
Gunnison, J.W. & W. Gilpin--Guide to the Kansas
   gold mines ...
Hall, E.H. --The Great West.
*Hall, J. (also OV-A2)--The Wilderness and the
   War Path.
Harmon, D.W. --Journal of voyages and travels
   in the interior of North America, ...
Hayden, F.V. --Contributions to the ethnography
   and philology of the Indian tribes of the Missouri
   Valley.
Henry, A. --Travels and adventures in Canada ...
Herne, P., pseud. --Perils and pleasures of a
   hunter's life.
*Hildreth, J. (also OV-A4)--Dragoon campaigns
   to the Rocky Mountains; ...
Hind, H.Y. --Narrative of the Canadian Red River
   exploring expedition ...
Holladay, B. --Table of distances of the Overland
   Daily Stage Line ...
Irving, Jr., J.T. --Indian sketches, ...
Jefferson, T. --Message from the President of the
   United States, ...
Kane, P. --Wanderings of an artist among the
   Indians of North America.
Kirker, J. --Don Santiago Kirker, ...
Langworthy, F. --Scenery of the plains, mountains
   and mines; ...
Latrobe, C.J. --The Rambler in North America.
Lee, D. & J.H. Frost--Ten years in Oregon.
Leland, A.--...Mining regions of Oregon and
   Washington ...
Lewis & Clark--...Expedition ... to the sources of
   the Missouri, ...

Lewis & Clark--Travels..performed i n the years
1804-1806, ...
McCormick, R.D.--Arizona: its resources and
prospects.
McCoy, I.--Remove Indians westward.
McCoy, I.--History of Baptist Indian Missions.
Marcou, J.--Geology of North America; ...
Morris, M.O.--Rambles in the Rocky Mountains; ...
Mullan, J.--Miners and travelers' guide to Oregon,
Murray, C.A.--Travels in North America ...
*Noel, T. (also CT)--Campaign from Santa Fe to
the Mississippi; ...
Nuttall, T.--Journal of travels into the Arkansas
Territory, ...
Owen, D.D.--Report of a geological survey of
Wisconsin, ...
Palliser, J.--Solitary rambles and adventures of
a hunter ...
Parker, S.--Rocky Mountain Indians.
*Pike, A. (also SB-1)--Prose sketches and poems.
Pike, Z.M.--Account of expeditions to the sources
of the Mississippi ...
Richardson, J.--Fauna Boreali-Americana; ...
Robinson, W.D.--Northwest Coast.
Ruxton, G.A.F.--Adventures in Mexico and the
Rocky Mountains.
Santa Fe Prisoners--Message from the President
of the U.S. ...
*Schoolcraft, H.R. (also TOS-2)--Journal of a
tour to the interior of Missouri and Arkansaw ...
Shively, J.M.--Route and distances to Oregon and
California, ...
Simpson, T.--...Discoveries on the North Coast
of America.
Slater, N.--Fruits of Mormonism, ...
Smet, P.J.--New Indian sketches.
Spalding, H.H.--Indians west of the Rocky Mountains.
Storrs, A.--Answers ... to certain queries ...
Stuart, G.--Montana as it is; ...
Sullivan, E.R.--Rambles and scrambles in North
and South America.
Tufts, J.--A tract descriptive of Montana Territory;
Udell, J.--Incidents of travel to California, ...
Upham, C.W.--Life explorations and public services
of John Charles Fremont.

*Webber, C.W. (also SB-1)--Gold mines of the Gila.
*Webber, C.W. (also SB-1)--Old Hicks the guide.
Wentworth, W.F.M. and W.B. Cheadle--The north-
   west passage by land.
West, J.--Journal ...
Winthrop, T.--John Brent.
*Wislizenus, F.A. (also OV-A5)--Ein Ausflug
   nach den Felsen-Gebirgen ...
Wislizenus, F.A.--...Tour to northern Mexico.
Wright, J.W.--Chivington's massacre of the
   Cheyenne Indians.

The Plains and the Rockies. Group 2. Per vol., as a
   group, 4.00 (106v.) LoC   1445
The titles in this series are:

   Aimard, G.--The Trail Hunter.
   American Enterprise--...Short account of the
      return trip ... from Astoria to St. Louis.
   Association de la Propagation de la Foi--Notice
      sur les Missions du Diocese de Quebec, ...
   Back, G.--...Arctic land expedition ...
   Ball, J.--Remarks upon the geology, and physical
      features of the country west of the Rocky Mountains.
   Bartlett, J.R.--Personal narrative of explorations
      and incidents in Texas, New Mexico, ...
   Bean, R. Expedition--Letter from Dr. J.S. Craig, ...
   Benjamin, I.J.--Drei Jahre in Amerika 1859-1862.
   Blanchet, A.M.A.--Mission de Walla-Walla.
   Blanchet, A.M.A.--Voyage de L'Eveque de Walla-Walla
   Blanchet, F.N.--Memoire presente à la S. Congrega-
      tion ...
   Blanchet, F.N.--Mission de la Colombie.
   Bolduc, J.B.Z.--Mission de la Colombie.
   Brackett, A.G.--History of the United States Cavalry,
   Brewerton, G.D.--A ride with Kit Carson ...
   Browne, J.R.--A tour through America.
   Campbell, A.H.--Pacific wagon roads.
   Carleton, J.H.--Diary of an excursion ... in New
      Mexico.
   Carleton, J.H.--The overland route to California.
   Clark, C.M.--A trip to Pike's Peak ...
   Clark, W.--Letter to his brother, ...
   Cook, P.S.G.--Report from the Secretary of War, ...
   Cortambert, L.R.--Voyage au pays des Osages.

Coyner, D.H. --The lost trappers; ...
Culbertson, T.A. --Journal of an expedition ... in
    1850.
Cutts, J.M. --The conquest of California and
    New Mexico, ...
Dix, J.A. --United States of America.
Demers, M. --Mission de Vancouver.
Domenech, E.H.D. --Seven years residence in the
    great deserts of North America.
Du Lac, F.M.P. --Voyage dans les deux Louisianes,
Dunbar, J. --Extracts from journal.
Dunn, J. --History of the Oregon Territory and
    British North-American fur trade; ...
Eastman, M.H. --The American annual.
Fergusson, D. --Letter of the Secretary of War, ...
Fort Kiowa Letter --Letter from one of Ashley's
    men, ...
Franklin, J. --...Second expedition to the shores
    of the Polar Sea, ...
Fremont, J.C. --Geographical memoir upon Upper
    California, ...
Glass, H. --Letters from the West.
Gold Mines In Kansas. Rand & Avery, 1859.
Great Central Route ... via Nebraska City.
Hall, E.H. --Hall's guide to the Great West.
Hayden, F.V. & J. Leidy--Geological sketch of
    the estuary and fresh water deposit forming the
    bad lands of the Judith River, ...
Hind, H.Y. --British North America.
Hind, H.Y. --North-West Territory.
Hind, H.Y. --...Topographical and geological
    exploration ... between Lake Superior, and
    Fort Garry, ...
Holdredge, S.M. --State, territorial and ocean guide
    book of the Pacific: ...
Holmes, R. --...Life of "Chee-ho-carte;"...
Horner, W.B. --Kansas and Nebraska gold regions, ...
Hughes, J.T. --Doniphan's expedition; ...
Hunter, J.D. --Manners and customs of several
    Indian tribes ...
Ives, J.C. --...The Colorado River of the West, ...
Jefferson, T. --President's Message.
Journey from New Orleans to California.
Kane, T.L. --The Mormons.
King, R. --...Journey to the shores of the Arctic
    Ocean, ...

Lafleche, R. --Lettre ... missionaire, à un de
   ses amis.
Lee, N. --Three years among the Camanches.
Leidy, J. --Notice of remains of extinct Vertebrata,
Lowell, D.W. & Co. --Map of the Nez Perces and
   Salmon River gold mines.
M'Donell, A. --...Transactions in the Red River
   Country, ...
Mackenzie, A. --Voyages from Montreal, ... to the
   Frozen and Pacific oceans; ...
Marcy, R.B. --Exploration of the Red River of
   Louisiana.
Marcy, R.B. --The prairie traveler.
Marryat, F. --...Travels and adventures of Monsieur
   Violet, ...
Military Gentleman--Notes on the Missouri River...
Mowry, S. --Geography and resources of Arizona
   and Sonora.
Nicaise, A. --Une année au desert.
Ogden, P.S. --Traits of American-Indian life and
   character.
Palmer, J. --Journal of travels over the Rocky
   Mountains.
Pattie, J.O. --Personal narrative...expedition from
   St. Louis.
Redpath, J. & R.J. Hinton--Hand-book to Kansas
   Territory and the Rocky Mountains' gold region;...
Roberts, S. --To emigrants to the Gold Region.
Robinson, J.S. --Sketches of the Great West.
Ruysdale, P. --Pilgrimage over the prairies.
Santa Fe and the Far West.
Simpson, G. --...Journey round the world, ...
Sitgreaves, L. --...Expedition down the Zuni and
   Colorado Rivers.
Stewart, W.G.D. --...Incidents of life and adventure
   in the Rocky Mountains.
Taylor, J.W. --Northwest British America and its
   relations to the State of Minnesota.
Thurston, S.R. --Geographical statistics. Oregon, ...
Wetmore, A. --Gazetteer of the State of Missouri.
Wyeth, J.B. --Oregon; ...

The Plains and the Rockies. Groups 3-5. in prep
   LoC   1446

161

Poey y Aloy, Felipe--Enumeratio piscium cubensium.
Madrid, 1875-76, and, Reviso piscium cubensium.
1880. (Reprint from Anales de la Sociedad Espanola
de Historia Natural, Vol. 9 (1880), pp. 243-61, and
plates). 2.00 F   1447

Polansky, David Lester (PE-381)--An evaluation of
selected physical education activities for college men;
a comparative analysis of physical education activities
to determine their educational potentials. 1957.
Thesis (Ed.D.), New York Univ. 207p. 1.85 O   1448

Pollard, Edward Alfred (S-B4)--Echoes from the South.
Comprising the most important speeches, proclamations,
and public acts emanating from the South during the
late war. New York, E.B. Treat & Co. (etc. etc.),
1866. ...211p. 3.95 LoC   1449

--------(S-B4)--Letters of the southern spy, in Washington
and elsewhere ... Baltimore, 1861. 91p. 3.95
LoC   1450

--------(S-B4)--The lost cause regained. New York,
G.W. Carleton & Co., 1868. ...214p. 3.95 LoC   1451

--------(S-B4)--The southern spy; or, Curiosities of
Negro slavery in the South. Letters from a southern
to a northern friend. Washington, H. Polkinhorn,
printer, 1859. 72p. 3.95 LoC   1452

Pomfrey, J.W. (KC-14)--A true disclosure and exposition
of the Knights of the golden circle, including the secret
signs, grips, and charges of the three degrees, as
practiced by the order. Cincinnati, printed for the
author, (c1861)...47p. 3.95 LoC   1453

Poore, B.P.--The conspiracy trial for the murder of the
president, and the attempt to overthrow the government
by the assassination of its principal officers. 3v.
10.00 SM   1454

Pope, John (TOS-3)--A tour through the southern and
western territories of the United States ... Richmond,
for the author, 1792. 5.95 LoC   1455

Popp, James Clark (PE-382)--Comparison of sophomore
high school boys who have high and low physical
fitness indices through case study procedures.
1959. Thesis (M.S.), Univ. of Oregon. 111p. 1.50
O   1456

Popp, Stephan (TOS-1)--Popp's Journal, 1777-1783;
by J.G. Rosengarten. Reprinted from the Pennsylvania
Magazine of History and Biography [April & July,
1902] Philadelphia, 1902. 5.95 LoC   1457

Porter, Duval (S-B4)--The poems of Duval Porter.
Lynchburg, Va., J.P. Bell & Co., 1875. vii,
275p. 3.95 LoC   1458

    Portuguese bibliographies--See Spanish and Portuguese
    bibliographies.

Post, Howard William--Chemistry of the aliphatic
orthoesters. 1943. ACS monograph no. 92. 5.60
MXT   1459

Power, Rodwell & Dew (LR-E&W)--Election. 2v. (1847-
56). MMP   1460

Pratt, William (TOS-4)--Journal ... 1695-1701. In
William L. Chaffin, History of the town of Easton,
Mass. Cambridge, J. Wilson & Son, 1866. 5.95
LoC   1461

Pratt's Contraband (LR-E&W)--Admiralty. 1v. (1740-
50). MMP   1462

Pre-1865 Law Reports [England and Wales] ... not in
English Reports (Reprint), together with certain
later scarce series.
Subs., 430. (1200.00) MMP   1463
The reports in this series (by reporter or title,
subject or court, with number of vols. and years
covered:
    Arnold, Common Pleas, 2v., 1838-39
    Arnold & Hodges, King's Bench, 1v., 1840-41
    Austin, County Court, 1v., 1867-69
    Bankruptcy & Insolvency Reports, Bankruptcy,
        2v., 1853-55

Barron & Arnold, Election, 1v., 1843-46
Barron & Arnold, Election, 1v., 1842
Bartholoman's Yorkshire Assize Cases, Assize,
    1v., 1811
Beavan & Walford, Railway, 1v., 1846
Bittleston, Chamber Cases, King's Bench, 1v.,
    1883-84
Bittleston, Wise & Parnell, Magistrates, 5v.,
    1844-50
Blackerby, Magistrates, 1v., 1505-1734
Bohun, Election, 1v., 1628-99
Bracton's Note Book, King's Bench, 3v., 1218-40
Brodrick & Freemantle, Ecclesiastical, 1v.,
    1840-64
Brooke, Ecclesiastical, 1v., 1850-72
Buck, Bankruptcy, 1v., 1816-20
Burrow, Settlement, 1v., 1732-76
Cababe & Ellis, Queen's Bench, 1v., 1882-85
Caldecott, Magistrates Cases, 1v., 1776-85
Carpmael, Patent, 3v., 1602-1840
Carrow, Hamerton & Allen, Magistrates Cases,
    4v., 1844-51
Cartmell, Trade Mark, 1v., 1876-92
Cases of Settlements & Removals, King's Bench,
    1v., 1685-1733
Charley's New Practice Cases, Practice 3v.,
    1875-81
Chitty, King's Bench, 2v., 1770-1822
Clayton's York Assizes, Assize, 1v., 1631-51
Clifford's Southwark, Election, 1v., 1796-97
Cockburn & Rowe, Election, 1v., 1833
Coltman, Registration, 1v., 1879-85
Common Law Reports, King's Bench, 3v., 1853-55
Corbett & Daniell, Election, 1v., 1819
Cox & Atkinson, Registration, 1v., 1843-46
Cox, Macrae & Hertslet, County Court, 3v.,
    1847-58
Creswell, Bankruptcy, 1v., 1827-29
Cripp's Church & Clergy, Ecclesiastical, 1v.,
    1847-50
Danson & Lloyd, Mercantile, 1v., 1828-29
Davies, Patent, 1v., 1785-1816
Davison & Merivale, King's Bench, 1v., 1828-44
Day's Election Cases, Election, 1v., 1892-93
Deacon, Bankruptcy, 4v., 1835-40

Deacon & Chitty, Bankruptcy, 4v., 1832-35
De Colyar, County Court, 1v., 1867-82
De Gex, Bankruptcy, 2v., 1844-50
De Gex, Macnaghten & Gordon, Bankruptcy, 1v.,
    1851-57
De Gex & Jones' Appeals, Bankruptcy, 1v., 1857-59
De Gex, Fisher & Jones, Bankruptcy, 1v., 1860
De Gex, Jones & Smith, Bankruptcy, 1v., 1862-65
Delane, Revision (Election), 1v., 1832-35
Douglas, Election, 4v., 1774-76
Dowling & Lowndes, Bail Court, 7v., 1843-49
Dowling & Ryland, King's Bench, 9v., 1822-27
Dowling & Ryland, Magistrates Cases, 4v., 1822-27
Dowling's Practice Cases, Bail, 9v., 1830-40
Dowling's Practice Cases, New Series, Bail, 2v.
    1841-42
Drinkwater, Common Pleas, 1v., 1840-41
Dunning, King's Bench, 1v., 1753-54
Eagle & Young, Tithe, 4v., 1204-1825
Equity Reports, Equity, 3v., 1853-55
Evans, King's Bench (Lord Mansfield's Civil
    Decisions), 2v., 1756-88
Falconer & Fitzherbert, Election, 1v., 1835-39
Fonblanque, Bankruptcy, 1v., 1849-52
Fox & Smith, Registration, 1v., 1886-95
Fraser, Election, 2v., 1790-92
Gale, Exchequer, 2v., 1835-36
Gale & Davidson, Queen's Bench, 3v., 1841-43
Glanville's Election Cases, Election, 1v., 1623-24
Glyn & Jameson, Bankruptcy, 2v., 1821-28
Goodeve, Patent, 1v., 1776-1883
Griffin, Patent, 1v., 1884-86
Griffin, Patent, 1v., 1885-87
Griffith, Poor Law, 1v., 1821-31
Gwillim's Tithe Cases, Tithe, 4v., 1224-1824
Harrison & Rutherford, Common Pleas, 1v.,
    1865-66
Harrison & Wollaston, Common Pleas, 2v., 1835-36
Hodges, Common Pleas, 3v., 1835-37
Holt's Admiralty Cases, Admiralty, 1v., 1863-67
Holt's Judgments in Ashby v. White & Re Patey et al.,
    King's Bench, 1v., 1702-05
Hopwood & Coltman, Registration, 2v., 1868-78
Hopwood & Philbrick, Registration, 1v., 1863-67
Horn & Hurlstone, Exchequer, 2v., 1838-39

Hurlstone & Walmsley, Exchequer, 1v., 1840-41
Joyce, Ecclesiastical, 1v., 1865-81
Keans & Grant's Appeals, Registration, 1v., 1854-62
Knapp & Ombler, Election, 1v., 1834-35
Lloyd & Welsby, Commercial, 1v., 1829-30
Lowndes & Maxwell, Bail, 1v., 1852-54
Lowndes, Maxwell & Pollock, Bail, 2v., 1850-51
Luder's Cases, Election, 3v., 1784-87
Lutwyche, Registration, 2v., 1843-53
Macrae & Hertslet, Bankruptcy, 2v., 1847-54
Macrory, Patent, 1v., 1852-55
Manning (Isle of Wight), Revision, 1v., 1832-35
Manning & Ryland, King' s Bench, 5v., 1827-30
Manning & Ryland, Magistrates Court, 3v., 1827-30
Maritime Law Cases (Crockford), Admiralty, 3v.,
    1860-71
Marshall, Common Pleas, 2v., 1813-16
Megone's Company Cases, Company, 2v., 1888-91
Monro, Acta Concellariae, Chancery, 1v., 1545-1625
Montagu, Bankruptcy, 1v., 1829-32
Montagu & Ayrton, Bankruptcy, 3v., 1833-38
Montague & Bligh, Bankruptcy, 1v., 1832-33
Montagu & Chitty, Bankruptcy, 1v., 1838-40
Montague, Deacon & De Gex, Bankruptcy, 3v.,
    1840-44
Montagu & McArthur, Bankruptcy, 1v., 1828-29
Moore, J.B., Common Pleas, 12v., 1817-27
Moore & Payne, Common Pleas, 5v., 1827-31
Moore & Scott, Common Pleas, 4v., 1831-34
Murphy & Hurlstone, Exchequer, 1v., 1836-37
Neville & Manning, King's Bench, 6v., 1832-36
Neville & Perry, King's Bench, 3v., 1836-38
Neville & Perry, Magistrate's Cases, 1v., 1836-37
New Practice Cases (Welford, Bittleston & Parnell),
    Bail, 3v., 1844-48
New Reports, All, 6v., 1862-65
Notes of Cases (ed. Thornton), Ecclesiastical &
    Maritime, 7v., 1841-59
Peckwell, Election, 2v., 1802-06
Perry's Insolvency, Bankruptcy, 1v., 1831
Perry & Davison, King's Bench, 4v., 1838-41
Philips' Election Cases, Election, 1v., 1780-81
Phillimore's Judgements, Ecclesiastical, 1v.,
    1867-75
Pigott & Rodwell, Registration, 1v., 1843-45

Placita Anglo-Normanica, --, 1v., 1066-1195
Power, Rodwell & Dow, Election, 2v., 1847-56
Pratt's Contraband, Admiralty, 1v., 1740-50
Price Practice Cases, Exchequer, 1v., 1830-31
Railways & Canal Cases, Railway, 7v., 1835-54
Rayner's Tithe Cases, Chancery, 3v., 1575-1782
Real Property & Conveyancing Cases (Welford
    Symons), Chancery, 2v., 1843-48
Ritchie, Reports by Francis Bacon, Chancery, 1v.,
    1617-21
Roberts, Leeming & Wallis, County Court, 1v.,
    1849-51
Robertson, Ecclesiastical, 2v., 1844-53
Roscoe's Prize Cases, Admiralty, 2v., 1745-1859
Rose, Bankruptcy, 2v., 1810-16
Rothery's Wreck Commissioners Judgements,
    Admiralty, 1v., 1876-80
Rowe's Interesting Cases, King's Bench, 1v.,
    1798-1823
Ryley's Placita Parliamentaria, Parliamentary,
    1v., 1290-1327
Saunders & Cole, Bail, 2v., 1846-48
Scott, Common Pleas, 8v., 1834-40
Scott's New Reports, Common Pleas, 8v., 1840-45
Searle & Smith, Probate & Divorce, 1v., 1859-60
Select Cases in Evidence, --, 1v., 1698-1732
Smith, J. P., King's Bench, 3v., 1803-06
Stillingfleet, Ecclesiastical, 2v., 1702-04
Tomlins, Election, 1v., 1689-1795
Tristram's Consistory Judgements, Ecclesiastical,
    1v., 1872-90
Tyrwhitt, Exchequer, 5v., 1830-35
Tyrwhitt & Granger, Exchequer, 1v., 1835-36
Webster, Patent, 2v., 1602-1855
Western's Tithe Cases, Tithe, 1v., 1535-1822
Willmore, Wollaston & Daveson, King's Bench,
    1v., 1837
Willmore, Wollaston & Hodges, King's Bench, 2v.,
    1838-39
Wolferstan & Bristowe, Election, 1v., 1859-65
Wolferstan & Dew, Election, 1v., 1856-58
Wollaston, Bail, 1v., 1840-41
Wood's Tithe Cases, Tithe, 4v., 1650-1798

Preston, William Campbell (S-B3)--Eulogy on Hugh
Swinton Legare; delivered, at the request of the city
of Charleston, Nov. 7, 1843. (Charleston, S.C.,
1843). 31p. 3.25 LoC   1464

Price Practice Cases (LR-E&W)--Exchequer. 1v.
(1830-31). MMP   1465

Priest, William (TOS-2)--Travels in the United States
of America; commencing in the year 1793, and
ending in 1797, ... London, printed for J. Johnson,
1802. 5.95 LoC   1466

Prince--Ahab's ivory house, form and technique in
"Moby-Dick." 1.40 KU   1467

The Prince Society. Vol. 1-36 (1865-1920). 205.60;
also available without Vol. 5-7 (offered by Peter
Smith), 193.48; single vols., 12.50 each   LoC   1468

Printz, Wolfgang Caspar--Compendium musicae signa-
toriae & modulatoriae vocalis. Dressden und Leipzig,
1714. 1.50 UR   1469

The pro-slavery argument (S-B4); as maintained by the
most distinguished writers of the Southern states,
containing the several essays on the subject of Chancellor
Harper, Governor Hammond, Dr. Sims, and Professor
Dew. Charleston, Walker, Richards & Co., 1852.
490p. 3.95 LoC   1470

Psychological Abstracts. Vols. 1-12 (1927-1938).
104.00   C   1471

Psychological Bulletins. Vols. 1-35 (1904-1938).
225.00   C   1472

Psychological Monographs. Vols. 1-36 (1895-1927).
170.00   C   1473

Pullan, Veronica Agnes--Simone Weil's criteria of the
sources of literary creativity. 1.05   KU   1474

Purviance, Levi (TOS-1)--The biography of the elder
David Purviance, with his memoirs...written by himself;
together with a historical sketch of the great Kentucky revival. Dayton, for the author, ...1848. 5.95 LoC   1475

Q

Quintano, Ricardo--The mind and art of Jonathan Swift.
3.20 SM   1476

R

Rafinesque, Constantine Samuel, 1783 (KC-14)--Also-
graphia Americana, or An American grove of new or
revised trees and shrubs of the genera myrica,
calycanthus, salix. Philadelphia, 1838. 76p. 3.95
LoC   1477

--------(KC-14)--American manual of the grape vines
and the art of making wine including an account of 69
species of vines. Philadelphia, printed for the author,
1830. ...64p. 3.95 LoC   1478

--------(KC-14)--American manual of the mulberry
trees. Their history, cultivation, properties, diseases,
species and varieties, etc., with hints on the production
of silk from their barks, etc. Philadelphia (Published
by the author for the Eleutherium of knowledge, no.5).
3.95 LoC   1479

--------(KC-14)--The American nations; or, Outlines of
their general history, ancient and modern. Philadelphia,
C.S. Rafinesque, 1836. 2v. in 1 3.95 LoC   1480

--------(KC-14)--Analyse de la nature; ou, Tableau de
l'universe et des corps organises. Palermo, Aux
depens de l'auteur, 1815. 224p. 3.95 LoC   1481

--------(KC-14)--The ancient monuments of North and
South America. 2d ed. cor., enl. and with some
additions. Philadelphia, printed for the author, 1838.
28p. 3.95 LoC   1482

--------(KC-14)--Annals of nature; or, Annual synopsis
of new genera and species of animals, plants, etc.,
discovered in North America. ... (Lexington, Ky.,
printed by T. Smith, 1820). 16p. 3.95 LoC   1483

--------(KC-14)--Caratteri di alouni nuovi generi e
nuove specie di animali e piante della Sicilia, con
varie osservazioni sopra i medesimi. Palermo,
per le stampe di San-filippo, 1810. ...105p. 3.95
LoC   1484

--------(KC-14)--Celestial wonders and philosophy, or,
The structure of the visible heavens with hints on their
celestial religion, and theory of futurity. Philadelphia,
printed for the Central Univ. of Ill., 1838. 135p.
3.95 LoC   1485

--------(KC-14)--Circular address on botany and zoology;
followed by the prospectus of two periodical works;
Annals of nature and Somiology of North America.
Philadelphia, printed for the author by S. Merritt,
1816. 36p. 3.95 LoC   1486

--------(KC-14)--Genius and spirit of the Hebrew Bible.
Philadelphia, printed for the Eleutherium of knowledge
(etc.), 1838. 264p. 3.95 LoC   1487

--------(KC-14)--The good book, and amenities of
nature, or Annals of historical and natural science.
Philadelphia, printed for the Eleutherium of knowledge,
1840. 84p. 3.95 LoC   1488

--------(KC-14)--Improvements of universities, colleges,
and other seats of learning or education in North America.
Philadelphia, printed for the Eleutherium of knowledge,
1839. ...48p. 3.95 LoC   1489

--------(KC-14)--Indice d'ittiologia siciliana ossia catalogo
metodico dei nomi latini, italiana, e siciliani dei
pesci, chi si renvengono in Sicilia disposti secondo un
metodo naturale eseguito da un appendice che contiene
la descrizione di alcuni nuovi pesci siciliani. Illustrato
da due piance. Messina, Presso Giovanni del Nobolo,
con approvazzione, 1810. 70p. 3.95   LoC   1490

--------(KC-14)--A monograph of the fluviatile bivalve
shells of the river Ohio, containing twelve genera and
sixty-eight species. Tr. from the French of C.S.
Rafinesque. Philadelphia, J. Dobson, 1832. ...72p.
3.95 LoC   1491

--------(KC-14)--Neogenyton, or Indication of sixty-six new genera of plants of North America. (Lexington, Ky.), 1825. 4p. 3.95 LoC   1492

--------(KC-14)--Outlines of a general history of North America. Second chronological part: colonial annals of the Antillan or West Indies islands ... Begun in Philadelphia in October 1827. 146p. 3.95 LoC   1493

--------(KC-14)--Sylva telluriana. Mantis, snyopt. New genera of trees and shrubs of North America. Being a supplement to Flora telluriana. Philadelphia, printed for the author and publisher, 1838. 184p. 3.95 LoC   1494

--------(KC-14)--The world, or Instability. A Poem ... Philadelphia, J. Dobson; London, O.Rich, 1836. 248p. 3.95 LoC   1495

Railways & Canal Cases (LR-E&W)--Railway. 7v. (1835-54). MMP   1496

The Rambler (TOS-2), or a tour through Virginia, Tennessee, Alabama, Mississippi and Louisiana; ... By a citizen of Maryland. Annapolis, printed by J. Green, 1828. 5.95 LoC   1497

Ramoneda, Ignacio--Arte de canto-llano en compendio breve. Madrid, 1778. 1.50 UR   1498

Ramos--An Andean vocabulary: a list of words of certain novels of the Andean region not found in dictionaries of Americanisms of Augusto Malaret or Francisco J. Santamaria. 1.40 KU   1499

Ramsay, Carl Albert--Tacheographia oder Geschwind-Schreibe-Kunst. Leipzig, 1743. Nr.500. MK   1500

Ramsay, David (TOS-2)--A sketch of the soil, climate, weather, and diseases of South-Carolina, ... Charleston, printed by W.P. Young, ... 1796. 5.95 LoC   . 1501

Rangazas, Ernest P. (PE-417)--A comparative analysis of selected college athletes and non-athletes on several hand-foot reaction-time measures. 1957. Thesis (M.S.), Indiana Univ. 111p. 1.40 O   1502

Rasch, Philip John (PE-396)..Effects of unilateral progressive resistance exercises on the contra-lateral limb. 1956. Thesis (Ph.D.), Univ. of Southern California. 121p. 1.65 O   1503

    Raymond, Grace (pseud.)--See Stillman, Annie Raymond

Rayner's Tithe Cases (LR-E&W)--Chancery. 3v. (1575-1782). MMP   1504

Read, Opie Percival (S-B4)--The carpetbagger; a novel by Opie Read & Frank Pixley. Chicago, Laird & Lee (c1899). 305p. illus. 3.95 LoC   1505

--------(KC-14)--A Kentucky Colonel. Chicago, F.J. Schulte & Co., 1890. 342p. 3.95 LoC   1506

--------(S-B4)--A Tennessee judge; a novel. Chicago, Laird & Lee, 1899. 325p. illus. 3.95 LoC   1507

Real Property and Conveyancing Cases (Welford Symons) (LR-E&W)--Chancery. 2v. (1843-48). MMP   1508

Reck, Baron Philipp-Georg Friedrich von (TOS-4)--An extract of the Journals of Mr. Commissary Von Reck ... and the Rev. Mr. Bolzius. London, M. Downing, 1734. 5.95 LoC   1509

Redpath, James & Richard J. Hinton (P&R-2)--Hand-book to Kansas Territory and the Rocky Mountains' gold region; ... and a preliminary treatise on the pre-emption laws of the United States. 5.95 LoC   1510

Reed, Isaac (TOS-1)--The Christian traveller. ...New-York, printed by J. & J. Harper, 1828. 5.95 LoC   1511

Reese, Lizette Woodworth (S-B3)--A branch of May. Baltimore, Cushing & Bailey, 1887. 42p. 3.25 LoC1512

--------(S-B4)--A quiet road. Boston & New York,
   Houghton, Mifflin & Co., 1896. x, 79p. 3.95 LoC   1513

   Reid, Christian (pseud.)--See Tiernan, Mrs.
      Frances Christine (Fisher)

Reid, John S. (OV-A5)--Gulzar; or, The rose-bower,
   a tale of Persia. Indianapolis, S. Turner (etc. etc.),
   1845. 212p. 4.32 LoC   1514

Reinhard, Leonhard--Kurzer und deutlicher unterricht
   von dem general-bass. Augspurg, 1750. 1.00 UR   1515

Reise von Hamburg nach Philadelphia (TOS-1). Hannover,
   Ritscherschen Buchhandlung, 1800. 5.95 LoC   1516

Relation de la Louisianne ou Mississippi (TOS-1). Ecrita
   à une dame, part un officier de marine. In Jean
   Frédéric Bernard, Relations de la Louisiane, ...
   Amsterdam, 1720. 5.95 LoC   1517

A relation of the successfulle beginnings of Lord Baltemore's
   Plantation in Mary-land (TOS-4); ... [London] Anno
   Domini 1634. 5.95 LoC   1518

Rells, Edmund W.--Zur Psychologie der Taschenspieler-
   kunst. Leipzig, 1893. Nr. 2. MK   1519

Report of the judge advocate general on "The Order of
   American Knights," alias "The Sons of Liberty."
   (AP-1). A western conspiracy in aid of the southern
   rebellion. Pub. by the Union Congressional Committee. Washington, D.C., Chronicle Print, 1864.
   16p. 2.45 LoC   1520

Reuter, Edward Richard (PE-397)--The relation of weight
   lifting performance to certain measures of body
   structure. 1957. Thesis (Ph.D.), Univ. of Illinois.
   122p. 1.65 O   1521

Revel, Gabriel Joachim du Perron, Comte de (TOS-4)--
   Journal particulier d'une compagne aux Indes Occidentales
   (1781-1782). ... Paris, H. Charles-Lavauzelle
   [1898?] 5.95 LoC   1522

Revel, James (TOS-1)--The poor unhappy transported felon's sorrowful account of his fourteen years transportation at Virginia in America. ... London, J. Marshall, 1764. 5.95 LoC   1523

Reynolds, John (TOS-2)--My own Times, embracing also the history of my life. Belleville, Ill., B.H. Perrymen & H.L. Davison, 1855. 5.95 LoC   1524

Reynolds, William--Ancestors and descendants of William and Elizabeth Reynolds of North Kingstown, R.I. By Thomas A. Reynolds. Philadelphia, 1903. 42p. 1.10 GML   1525

Ribet, Emily Catherine (PSY-87)--Teaching techniques used with fear cases in beginning swimming for college women. 1957. Thesis (M.Ed.), Woman's College, Univ. of North Carolina. 83p. 1.25 O   1526

El ricettario dell 'arte, et vniversita de medici, et spetiali della citta di Firenze (HS-1) Fiorenza, L. Torrentino, stampator dvcale, 1550. 186, 10 1 3.54 LoC   1527

Rich, R. (TOS-3)--Nevves from Virginia. The lost Flocke Triumphant. ... London, printed by Edw: Allde, ... 1610. 5.95 LoC   1528

Richards, Dorothy M. (PSY-118)--A study of social integration in high school physical education classes. 1958. Thesis (Ed.M.), Pennsylvania State Univ. 45p. 1.15 O   1529

Richardson, Albert D. (MFM)--Beyond the Mississippi. 1867. 572p. 7.78 LoC   1530

Richardson, John (TOS-1)--An account of the life of ... John Richardson, ... and his services in the work of the ministry, ... London, printed and sold by Luke Hinde, 1757. 5.95 LoC   1531

--------(P&R-1)--Fauna Boreali-Americana; or the zoology of the northern parts of British America: containing descriptions ... collected on the late northern land expeditions under command of Capt. Sir John Franklin. 4v. 5.95 each LoC   1532

Richter, Heinz William (RC-40)--The effects of recreation
therapy on mentally ill patients. 1957. Thesis (M.S.),
Univ. of Utah. 103p. 1.40 O   1533

Rice, David (KC-8)--An essay on baptism. Baltimore,
Printed by Wm. Goddard, in Market Street, 1789.
82p. 2.89 LoC   1534

--------(KC-9)--A Kentucky protest against slavery.
Slavery inconsistent with justice and good policy, proved
by a speech, delivered in the convention, held at
Danville, Ky.   New York, printed by Samuel Wood,
1812. (New York) Pub. at the office of the Rebellion
Record (1864?). 13p. 2.50 LoC   1535

Riedesel, Friederike Charlotte Luise (von Massow)
Freifrau von (TOS-3)--Auszuge aus den briefen und
papieren des generals freyherrn von Riedesel und seiner
gemalinn, ... Reuss [Berlin] Gedruckt als manuscript
für die familie [1800] 5.95 LoC   1536

Ritchie, Reports by Francis Bacon (LR-E&W)--Chancery.
1v. (1617-21). MMP   1537

Ritson, Mrs. Anne (TOS-2)--A poetical picture of
America, being of observations made, during a residence
of several years, at Alexandria, and Norfolk, in Virginia;
... from the year 1799 to 1807. By a lady. London,
printed for the author ... 1809. 5.95 LoC   1538

Rivera, Pedro de (Villalón) (TOS-4)--Diario y Derrotero
de lo caminado, visto y observado en el discurso de
la visita general de Precidios, situados en las Provincias
Ynternas de Nueva España. Guatemala, 1736. 5.95
LoC   1539

Robb, James, 1814 (AP-1)--A southern confederacy.
Letter by J. Robb, late a citizen of New Orleans, to
Hon. Alexander H. Stephens, of Ga. Chicago, J.S.
Thompson, 1863. 17p. 2.45 LoC   1540

Roberts--The tales and songs of the Couch family.
3.15 KU   1541

Roberts, Sidney (P&R-2)--To emigrants to the Gold Region.
   A treatise, showing the best way to California, ...
   with the Constitution and Articles of Agreement, of the
   Joint Stock Mutual Insurance Merchandizing Co. 5.95
   LoC   1542

Roberts, Leeming & Wallis (LR-E&W)--County Court.
   1v. (1849-51). MMP   1543

Robertson (LR-E&W)--Ecclesiastical. 2v. (1844-53).
   MMP   1544

Robertson, George (KC-9)--An address delivered at Camp
   Madison, on the Fourth of July, 1843. Frankfort,
   Ky., Hodges, Todd & Pruett, printers, 1843. 32p.
   2.50 LoC   1545

Robien, Gerhard Carl, Jr. (HE-44)--A study of three
   types of preventive ankle taping. 1954. Thesis
   (M.S.), Univ. of Wisconsin. 52p. 1.05 O   1546

Robinson, Ebenezer--A historical sketch of the Robinson
   family of the line of Ebenezer Robinson, ... By Mrs.
   Jane M. (Bancroft) Robinson. Detroit, Mich., 1903.
   viii, 5, 68p. 1.40 GML   1547

Robinson, Jacob S. (P&R-2)--Sketches of the Great West.
   5.95 LoC   1548

Robinson, John Hovey (S-B4)--The house of silence.
   A tale of New Orleans. New York, Street & Smith,
   1890. 232p. 3.95 LoC   1549

--------(S-B3)--Marion's Brigade; or, The light dragoons.
   A tale of the Revolution. Boston, F. Gleason's Pub.
   Hall, 1852. 7, 100 p. 3.25 LoC   1550

--------(S-B3)--Milrose; or, The cotton-planter's daughter.
   A tale of South Carolina. New York, F.A. Brady
   (c1862). 110p. 3.25 LoC   1551

--------(S-B3)--The Lone Star; or, The Texas brave.
   A tale of the Southwest. Boston, F. Gleason's Pub.
   Hall, 1852. 7, 100p. 3.25 LoC   1552

--------(S-B3)--The White Rover; or, The lovely maid
of Louisiana. A romance of the wild forest. New York,
S. French (c1851). 7, 100p. 3.25 LoC   1553

Robinson, Margie C. (HE-45)--Measuring the sex
knowledge of junior high school pupils. 1949. Thesis
(M.A.), Univ. of Oregon. 118p. 1.50 O   1554

Robinson, William Davis (P&R-1)--Northwest Coast.
National Intelligencer (tri-weekly issue), Jan. 27, 1821,
reprinted in Niles Register, March 10, 1821. 5.95
LoC   1555

Rochambeau, Jean Baptiste Donatien de Vimeur, Comte
de (TOS-4)--Memoires militaires, historiques et
politiques ... Paris, Fain [etc.], 1809. 2v. 5.95
each LoC   1556

Rochefort, Charles de (TOS-4)--Histoire naturelle et
morale des iles Antilles de l'Amerique. ... Roterdam,
A Leers, 1658. 5.95 LoC   1557

--------(TOS-4)--Recit de l'estat present des celebres
colonies ... Rotterdam, R. Leers, 1681. 5.95 LoC1558

Rochelle, Rene Herman (PH-66)--Venous blood pressure
measurements during exercise by the strain gauge and
pressure amplifier method. 1953. Thesis (Ph.D.),
Univ. of Illinois. 115p. 1.40 O   1559

Rogers, of Maine--The Rogers family of Georgetown,
Me. By Josiah H. Drummond. 1897. 37p. 1.10
GML   1560

Roney, Phyllis Carolyn (PE-418)--Some factors of
kinesthesis and relaxation. 1960. Thesis (Ph.D.),
Univ. of Oregon. 108p. 1.40 O   1561

Ronning, Hilding Earl (PE-441)--Wall tests for evaluating
tennis ability. 1959. Thesis (M.S.), State College
of Washington. 53p. 1.15 O   1562

Roscoe's Prize Cases (LR-E&W)--Admiralty. 2v.
(1745-1859). MMP   1563

Rose (LR-E&W)--Bankruptcy. 2v. (1810-16). MMP   1564

Rose, Dorothy Lou (PE-442)--The effect of the obliquity of
the shaft of the femur in women upon speed of running
and vertical jumping ability. 1959. Thesis (M.S.),
Pennsylvania State Univ. 62p. 1.15 O   1565

Rosecrans, William Starke, 1819 (AP-1)--Letters from
Gen. Rosecrans to the democracy of Indiana. Action
of the Ohio regiments, at Murfreesboro, regarding
the copperheads. Philadelphia, printed for the Union
League, 1863. 7, 1p. 2.45 LoC   1566

Rosenstengel, J.J.--Elementa Chymiae Methodo Conscripta
Mathematica. Supplementa Beccheriana. Frankfurt
a.M., 1716. Nr.63-65. MK   1567

Rothery's Wreck Commissioners Judgements (LR-E&W)--
Admiralty. 1v. (1876-80). MMP   1568

Rouse, J. (AP-1)--Horrible massacre at Guyandotte,
Va., and a journey to the rebel capital, with a description
of prison life in a tobacco warehouse at Richmond.
(N.p.), 1862. 56p. 2.45 LoC   1569

Rowe's Interesting Cases (LR-E&W)--King's Bench.
1v. (1798-1823). MMP   1570

Rowland, Kate Mason (S-B4)--The life of Charles Carroll
of Carrollton, 1737-1832, with his correspondence and
public papers. New York & London, G.P. Putnam's
Sons, 1898. 2v. illus. 3.95 each LoC   1571

Rozier, Firman A. (MFM)--Rozier's history of the early
settlements of the Mississippi Valley. 1890. 337p.
5.20   LoC   1572

Ruffin, Edmund (S-B3)--African colonization unveiled.
Washington, Printed by L. Towers (1859?). 3.25
LoC   1573

--------(S-B3)--The political (!) [sic] economy of slavery;
or, the institution considered in regard to its influence
on public wealth and general welfare. (Washington),
Printed by L. Towers (1857?). 31p. 3.25 LoC   1574

Russel, R.R.--Economic aspects of Southern sectionalism,
   1840-1861. 2.75   SM   1575

Ruxton, George Augustus Frederick (P&R-1)--Adventures
   in Mexico and the Rocky Mountains. 5.95   LoC   1576

Ruysdale, Philip (P&R-2)--A pilgrimage over the prairies.
   2v. 5.95 each LoC   1577

Rylander, Curtis Roy (PE-443)--The construction and
   validation of measurement procedures for the college
   program of physical education for men. 1959. Thesis
   (Ph.D.), New York Univ. 328p. 2.45 O   1578

Ryley's Placita Parliamentaria (LR-E&W). Parliamentary.
   1v. (1290-1327). MMP   1579

                              S

Sachs, Hans--Standebuch. Holzschnitte von Jost Amman.
   Frankfurt a.M., 1568. Nr.317-318.   MK   1580

St. Clair, Janet (RC-46)--The education curriculum
   philosophy of a select group of school camps. 1958.
   Thesis (M.A.), State Univ. of Iowa. 73p. 1.15 O   1581

St. Franciscus--Laudes Creaturarum.   London,
   Doves Press, 1910. Nr. 195. MK   1582

St. John, Percy Bolingbroke, 1821 (KC-11)--Queen of the
   woods; or, The Shawnee captives. A romance of the
   Ohio. New York, Beadle & Co. (1868). 129p. (Beadle's
   dime novels, no. 174). 2.91   LoC   1583

Sadlo, Lola Marie (RC-41)--An exploration of factors
   related to leadership of recreation directors in
   selected major cities, as determined by biographical
   data. 1957. Thesis (Ed.D.), Univ. of Southern
   California. 410p. 3.00 O   1584

Safford, William Harrison, 1821 (KC-12)--The life of
Harman Blennerhassett. Comprising an authentic
narrative of the Burr expedition; and containing many
additional facts not heretofore published. Chillicothe, O.,
Ely, Allen & Looker, 1850. 239p. 4.12 LoC   1585

Saladino da Ascoli, 15th cent. (HS-1)--[Domini Saladini
de esculo Serenitati principis Tarenti phisici principalis
Compedij aromatariorum opus feliciter incipit.
Colophon: Impressum Ferrarie per prouidum virum
magistrum Andream gallum (i.e. Andreas Belfortis)
1488] 42p. 2.95   LoC   1586

Salmon, E.S.--A monograph of the erysiphaceae. 1.10
MMe   1587

Salmon, Thomas (TOS-4)--The universal traveller; or,
A compleat description of the several nations of the
world: ... London, printed for R. Baldwin, 1752-53.
2v. 5.95 each LoC   1588

Salter, John--John Salter, mariner. By Wm. T. Salter.
Philadelphia, 1900. 58p. 1.10 GML   1589

Santa Fe and the Far West (P&R-2)--Niles National Register,
Dec. 4, 1841, Vol. LXI, page 209. 5.95 LoC   1590

Santa Fe Prisoners (P&R-1)--Message from the President
of the United States, transmitting in compliance with
a resolution of the House of Representatives, ... information relative to the arrest and imprisonment of
certain American citizens at Santa Fe, by authority
of the Government of Spain, April 15, 1818. Read, and
ordered to lie on the table. 5.95 LoC   1591

Sapora, Allen V. (RC-42)--A recreation survey of the
Rockford Park District, Rockford, Ill. 1955. 207p.
2.05 O   1592

Sargent, Winthrop, ed. (TOS-4)--The history of an
expedition against Fort Du Quesne, in 1755; ... Ed.
from the original mss. ... Philadelphia, Lippincott,
Grambo & Co., 1855. 5.95 LoC   1593

Saugrain de Vigni, Antoine Francois (TOS-4)--L'Odysée
Américaine d'une famille francaise ... Baltimore,
The Johns Hopkins Press, 1936. 5.95 LoC   1594

Saunders & Cole (LR-E&W)..Bail. 2v. (1846-48).
MMP   1595

Sauter, Waldo E. (PE-419)--An evaluation of the undergraduate professional preparation in physical education
for men in selected colleges and universities in Indiana.
1957. Thesis (P.E.D.), Indiana Univ. 234p.
2.05 O   1596

Savage, John--Family of John Savage of Middletown,
Conn., 1652. By James F. Savage. Boston, 1894.
41p. 1.10 GML   1597

Say, Thomas (OV-A5)--American conchology; or description of the shells of North America. New Harmony,
Ind., Printed at the School press, 1830-34. 240p.
4.63 LoC
--------A glossary to Say's Conchology. New Harmony,
Ind., Printed by R. Beck & J. Bennett, 1832.
25p. 2.50 LoC   1598

--------(OV-A5)--American entomology, or description
of the insects of North America. (Philadelphia)
Philadelphia Museum, S.A. Mitchell, 1824-28. 3v.
v1, 3.50; v2, 2.50; v3, 2.50 LoC   1599

Scannell, Robert James (PH-68)--Selected factors
concerned with the maintenance of endurance. 1959.
Thesis (M.S.), Pennsylvania State Univ. 114p. 1.40
O   1600

Scharf, John Thomas (MFM)--History of St. Louis City
and County. 1883. 2v. 15.90 LoC   1601

Schermerhorn, John Freeman (TOS-3)--A correct view
of that part of the United States which lies west of the
Allegany mountains, with regard to religion and
morals. ... Hartford, P.B. Gleason & Co., printers,
1814. 5.95 LoC   1602

Schick, Frank L.--Board librarian relationships in American
public libraries 1948. Thesis (M.S.), Univ. of Chicago.
1.40 KU   1603

Schlaadt, Richard Grover (PSY-101)--The physical activity
   habits of individuals and how by example they influence
   the physical activity habit patterns of others. 1958.
   Thesis (M.S.), Univ. of Illinois. 51p. 1.15 O   1604

Schlatter, Michael (TOS-4)--Getrouw Verhaal van den
   waren Toestant der meest herderloze Gemeentens in
   Pensylvanien en aangrensende Provintien, ... T'Amstel-
   dam, by Jacobus Loveringh, Boekverkoper voor aan
   op den Nieuwendyk, 1751. 5.95 LoC   1605

Schmidt, Friedrich (TOS-1)--Versuch über den politischen
   Zustand der Vereinigten Staaten von Nord-Amerika ...
   Stuttgart und Tübingen, J.G. Cotta, 1822. 2v.
   5.95 each LoC   1606

Schoepf, Johann David, 1752-1800 (HS-1)--Materia medica
   Americana potissimvm regni vegetabilis. Erlangae,
   Svmtibvs I.I.Palmii, 1787. 170p. 3.36 LoC   1607

Schoolcraft, Henry Rowe (TOS-1)--The Indian in his
   wigwam, ... Buffalo, Derby & Hewson, 1848. 5.95
   LoC   1608

--------(P&R-1, also TOS-2)--Journal of a tour to the
   interior of Missouri, and Arkansaw ... toward the
   Rocky Mountains, performed in the years 1818-19.
   London, Sir Richard Phillips & Co., 1821. 5.95
   LoC   1609

--------(TOS-3)--Travels in the central portion of the
   Mississippi valley; ... New York, Collins & Hannay,
   1825. 5.95 LoC   1610

--------(TOS-3)--A view of the lead mines of Missouri...
   New York, Charles Wiley & Co., 1819. 5.95 LoC   1611

Schopf, Johann David (TOS-2)--Reise durch einige der
   mittlern und Südlichen Vereinigten nordamerikanischen
   Staaten nach Ost-Florida und den Bahama-Inseln
   unternommen in den jahren 1783 und 1784 ... Erlangen,
   J.J. Palm, 1788. 2v. 5.95 each LoC   1612

Schroeder, Georgia Ellen (PSY-119)--The relationship
of social acceptance, motor performance, and intelligence
to children's activity choices. 1959. Thesis (M.A.),
State Univ. of Iowa. 105p. 1.40 O   1613

Schultz, Alden Edwin (PE-420)--The effect of a wrestling
program on balance in college physical education
classes and amongst members of a college wrestling
squad. 1959. Thesis (M.S.), South Dakota State College.
47p. 1.15   O   1614

Schultz, Christian (TOS-3)--Travels on an Inland voyage
through the states ... performed in the years 1807-08.
... New York, printed by Isaac Riley, 1810. 5.95
LoC   1615

Schwab, J.C.--Confederate States of America, 1861-
65. 3.00 SM   1616

Science Progress. Vol. 45 (1957). 4.4. MMe   1617

Scott (LR-E&W)--Common Pleas. 8v. (1834-40).
MMP   1618

Scott, Job (TOS-1)--Journal of the life, travels and
gospel labours, ... New York, Isaac Collins, 1797.
5.95   LoC   1619

Scott, Joseph (TOS-3)--The United States gazetteer: ...
Philadelphia, F. & R. Bailey, 1795. 5.95 LoC   1620

Scott's New Reports (LR-E&W)--Common Pleas. 8v.
(1840-45). MMP   1621

Scotus Americanus, pseud. (TOS-1)--Informations concerning the province of North Carolina, ... By an
impartial hand. ... Glasgow, printed for James Knox...
and Charles Elliot ... Edinburgh, 1773. 5.95 LoC 1622

Scribonius Largus (HS-1). De compositione medicamentoru
liber, iampridem Io. Rvellii opera e tenebris erutus,
& a situ uindicatus. [Basileae] Apud A. Cratandrvm,
1529. 318p. Bound with Joannes Actuarius. De vrinis
...Basileae [1529] 8.99   LoC   1623

Scull Fam.--The family of Scull (of N.Y., N.J. and Pa.).
   By Wm. E. Scull. Philadelphia, 1930. 53p. 1.10
   GML   1624

Searight, T.B.--The Old Pike, a history of the National
   Road. 4.00 SM   1625

Searle & Smith (LR-E&W)--Probate & Divorce. 1v.
   (1859-60). MMP   1626

Select Cases in Evidence (LR-E&W). 1v. (1698-1732).
   MMP   1627

Serdula, George (HE-53)--Standardization of a first aid
   knowledge test for college students. 1957. Thesis
   (D. of Health & Safety), Indiana Univ. 147p. 2.05 O 1628

Serial Atlas of the Marine Environment: a geographic
   journal of biological and physical oceanography.
   "Background material ... being reproduced on Microcards:" U.S. Fish Commission. Bulletin. Vols.
   VII & XX. AmG   1629

Sessoms, Hanson Douglas (RC-36)--A glossary of selected
   public recreation terms. 1954. Thesis (M.S.),
   Univ. of Illinois. 56p. 1.15 O   1630

Sewall, Samuel--Diary, 1674-1729. 3v. 14.00 SM   1631

Seward, William (TOS-2)--Journal of a voyage from
   Savannah to Philadelphia, and from Philadelphia to
   England. London, J. Oswald, 1740. 5.95 LoC   1632

Seymour, Clara--The Seymour family (ancestors of
   Clara E. Seymour). By Tyler S. Morris. Chicago,
   1900. 147, 181p. .80 GML   1633

Seymour, William (TOS-2)--...A journal of the southern
   expedition, 1780-1783. ... Wilmington, The Hist.
   Society of Delaware, 1896. 5.95 LoC   1634

Sharan, James (TOS-2)--Adventures ... Baltimore,
   printed by G. Dobbin & Murphy, ... for J. Sharan,
   1808   5.95 LoC   1635

Shaw, [George] Bernard. Collected works. Ed. by Dan
  H. Laurence. approx. 75.00 RDX   1636

Shaw, Joshua (TOS-3)--United States directory for the
  use of travellers and merchants, ... Philadelphia,
  printed by J. Maxwell [1822] 5.95 LoC   1637

Shea, George, 1826 (AP-1)--Jefferson Davis: a statement
  concerning the imputed special cause of his long
  imprisonment by the government of the United States,
  ... London, E. Stanford, 1877. 20p. 2.45 LoC   1638

Sheehan, Thomas Joseph (PSY-88)--Attitudes of senior
  male students at the Ohio State University concerning
  the athlete and intercollegiate competition. 1956.
  Thesis (M.A.), Ohio State Univ. 85p. 1.25 O   1639

Shelley, Morgan E. (PE-421)--Maturity, structure,
  strength, motor ability, and intelligence test profiles
  of outstanding elementary school and junior high school
  athletes. 1960. Thesis (M.S.), Univ. of Oregon.
  310p. 2.45 O   1640

Shively, J.M. (P&R-1)--Route and distances to Oregon
  and California, ... 5.95 LoC   1641

Silva, Sister M. Frances Clare(ACRL-108)--A history of
  Ursuline College Library, Cleveland, Ohio, 1922-
  1957. 1958. Thesis (M.S. in L.S.), Western Reserve
  Univ. .75 UR   1642

Simms, William Gilmore (S-B3)--Areytos; or, Songs of
  the South. Charleston, J. Russell, 1846. 9,108p.
  3.25 LoC   1643

--------(S-B4)--As good as a comedy; or, The
  Tennessean's story. By an editor. Philadelphia,
  A.Hart, 1852. ...251p. 3.95 LoC   1644

--------(S-B3)--Atlantis. A story of the sea; in three
  parts. New York, J. & J. Harper, 1832. 80p. 3.25
  LoC   1645

--------(S-B4)--The city of the silent; a poem. Delivered
  at the consecration of Magnolia cemetery. Nov. 19, 1850.
  54p. 3.95 LoC   1646

--------(S-B4)--The geography of South Carolina: being
a companion to the history of that state. Charleston,
Babcock & Co., 1843. ...192p. 3.95 LoC   1647

--------(S-B3)--The golden Christmas: a chronicle of
St. John's, Berkeley. Comp. from the notes of a
briefless barrister, ... Charleston, Walker, Richards
& Co., 1852. 168p. 3.25 LoC   1648

--------(S-B4)--The history of South Carolina, from its
first European discovery to its erection into a republic:
with a supplementary chronicle of events to the present
time. Charleston, S. Babcock & Co., 1840. ...355p.
3.95   LoC   1649

--------(S-B4)--The lily and the totem; or, The Huguenots
in Florida. A series of sketches, picturesque and historical, of the colonies of Coligni, in North America,
1562-1570. ... New York, Baker & Scribner, 1850.
xi, 470p. 3.95 LoC   1650

--------(S-B4)--Sack and destruction of the city of
Columbia, S.C. To which is added a list of the property
destroyed. Columbia, S.C., Power Press of the
Daily Phoenix, 1865. 76p. 3.95 LoC   1651

--------(S-B4)--South Carolina in the Revolutionary War;
being a reply to certain misrepresentations and mistakes
of recent writers in relation to the course and conduct
of this state. ... Charleston, S.C., Walker & James,
1853. 177p. 3.95 LoC   1652

Simone, Anthony (PE-422)--The socio-economic status of
intercollegiate athletes. 1953. Thesis (Ph.D.),
Univ. of Utah. 151p. 1.65 O   1653

Simpson, George (P&R-2)--Narrative of a journey round
the world, during the years 1841-42. 2v. 5.95
each LoC   1654

Simpson, Thomas (P&R-1)--Narrative of the discoveries
on the North Coast of America; ... during the years
1836-39. 5.95 LoC   1655
    Singleton, Arthur (pseud.)--See Knight, Henry
    Cogswell.

Sitgreaves, Lorenzo (P&R-2)--Report of an expedition down
the Zuni and Colorado Rivers. 5.95 LoC   1656

Slater, Nelson (P&R-1)--Fruits of Mormonism, or a fair
and candid statement of facts ... by more than forty
eyewitnesses. 5.95 LoC   1657

Slaughter, Philip (S-B3)--A history of Bristol Parish,
Va., with genealogies of families connected therewith,
and historical illustrations. 2d. ed. Richmond,
J.W. Randolph & English, 1879. 237p. 3.25 LoC   1658

--------(S-B3)--A history of St. Mark's Parish, Culpeper
county, Virginia, with notes on old churches and old
families, and illustrations of the manners and customs
of olden time. Baltimore, Innes & Co., printers,
1877. 200p. 3.25 LoC   1659

Slaymaker, Thomas E. (PH-69)--The effect of liquid
consumption during a brief rest period on a second bout
of exhaustive exercise. 1959. Thesis (M.S.),
Pennsylvania State Univ. 38p. 1.15 O   1660

Sluiter, Floyd V. (PE-423)--The attitudes of men students
toward the required physical education program at
South Dakota State College. 1959. Thesis (M.S.),
South Dakota State College. 62p. 1.15 O   1661

Smet, Pierre-Jean de (P&R-1)--New Indian sketches,
5.95 LoC   1662

Smith, Britta Helen (ACRL-121)--University library collections as inducements for recruitment of faculty personnel.
1959. Thesis (M.A.), Emory Univ. .75 UR   1663

Smith, Daniel (TOS-3)--Journal ... with introd. and
notes by S.G.L. Sioussat. ...[Nashville, 1915] 5.95
LoC   1664

Smith, Edmund Kirby, 1824-1893 (AP-1)--History of
Gen. Edmund Kirby Smith. New York, Knapp & Co.,
c1888. 15p. 2.45 LoC   1665

Smith, Eli, 1787 (KC-14)--A funeral sermon on the death of Gov. Madison, delivered before the legislature of Kentucky and the citizens of Frankfort, Dec. 8th, 1818. Frankfort, Ky., Gerald & Kendall, printers, 1817. 26p. 3.95 LoC   1666

Smith, Francis Hopkinson (S-B4)--A day at Laguerre's and other days; being nine sketches. Boston & New York, Houghton, Mifflin & Co., 1892. ...190p. 3.95 LoC   1667

--------(S-B4)--A gentleman vagabond and some others. Cambridge, Printed at the Riverside Press, 1895. 182p. 3.95 LoC   1668

Smith, Goldwin, 1823 (AP-1)--England and America. Manchester, A. Ireland & Co., 1865. 36p. 2.45 LoC   1669

Smith, Henry Clay (KC-11)--Outline history of the wilderness of Kentucky and the religious movements of the early settlers of our country and the church history of the North Middletown community. Paris, Ky., Frank Remington, printer, 1923. 91p. 2.50 LoC   1670

Smith, Hubbard Madison (OV-A5)--At midnight and other poems. Indianapolis, Ind., Carlon & Hellenbeck, printers, 1898. 176p. 3.93 LoC   1671

Smith, J. P. (LR-E&W)--King's Bench. 3v. (1803-06). MMP   1672

Smith, James (TOS-1)--An account of the remarkable occurrences ... during his captivity with the Indians, in the years 1755, ... ' 59, ... Written by himself. Lexington, John Bradford, 1799. 5.95 LoC   1673

Smith, James (OV-A5)--Poems by James Smith and J.R. Smith, with an autobiography. Cincinnati, Ohio, Elm Street Prtg. Co., 1890. 202p. 4.21 LoC   1674

Smith, John (TOS-1)--A map of Virginia. With a description of the cvntrey, the commodities, people, government and religion. ... At Oxford, printed by Joseph Barnes, 1612. 5.95 LoC   1675

--------(TOS-4)--A true relation of such occurrences
and accidents of noate as hath hapned in Virginia ...
London, printed for John Tappe, ...1608. 5.95 LoC1676

Smith, Robert--Harmonics, or the philosophy of musical
sounds. Cambridge, 1749. 2.25 UR   1677

Smith, Samuel (TOS-4)--Memoirs... from 1776 to 1786.
Middleborough, Mass., 1853. 5.95 LoC   1678

Smith, Warren Ellison (HE-54)-- The health worries of
961 public high school seniors in Oregon. 1957.
Thesis (Ed.D.), Stanford Univ. 169p. 1.90 O   1679

Smith, William Loughton (TOS-4)--Journal,..1790-91,
ed. by A. Matthews. Cambridge, The University
Press, 1917. 5.95 LoC   1680

Smith, William Russell (S-B4)--The chief. A poem in ten
epistles, containing some political hints ...Washington,
1881. 37, 2p. 3.95 LoC   1681

--------(S-B4)--Reminscences of a long life; historical,
political, personal and literary. Vol. I. Washington,
D.C., W.R. Smith, Sr. (c1889). 375p. illus. 3.95
LoC   1682

--------(S-B3)--The Royal Ape: a dramatic poem.
Richmond, West & Johnston, 1863. 85p. 3.25 LoC 1683

Smithwick, Noah (S-B4)--The evolution of a state; or,
Recollections of old Texas days ... Comp. by his
daughter Nanna Smithwick Donaldson. Austin, Texas,
Gammel Book Co. (c1900). 9,354p. illus. 3.95
LoC   1684

Smyth, John Ferdinand Dalziel (TOS-2)--A tour in the
United States of America: ... London, for G. Robinson
[etc.], 1784. 2v. 5.95 each LoC   1685

Soares, Patricia Louise (PSY-98)--A study of the relationship between selected elements of coordination and
the rate of learning complex motor skills. 1958.
Thesis (Ed.M.), Woman's College, Univ. of North
Carolina. 100p. 1.40 O   1686

Some considerations on the consequences of the French
    settling colonies on the Mississippi (TOS-4), ...
    From a gentleman in America to his friend in London.
    ... London, Printed for J. Roberts, 1720. 5.95
    LoC   1687

The Somers Tracts. 2d ed. Rev., augmented and
    arranged by Walter Scott. London, Printed for T.
    Cadell & W. Davies (etc.), 1809-1815. 13v. 249.95;
    single vols., 20.95 each LoC   1688

Soule, Roger Gilbert (PSY-99)--The effect of badminton
    and handball on tennis ability of inexperienced players.
    1958. Thesis (M.S.), Univ of Illinois. 59p. 1.15
    O   1689

The Southern Literary Messenger; devoted to every
    department of literature and the fine arts ... Vol.
    1-38 (Aug. 1834-June 1864). 346.80; single vols.,
    12.00 each LoC   1690

Spalding, Henry Harmon (P&R-1)--Indians west of the
    Rocky Mountains. Missionary Herald, Boston, vol.
    33, 1837. 5.95 LoC   1691

Spanish and Portuguese bibliographies; the major national
    bibliographies ... published prior to 1900, with emphasis
    on the ... works of Jose Toribio Medina.:
        South America (10,274pp.) 52.00
        Latin America, general (4,724pp.) 24.00
        Mexico & Guatemala (11, 503pp.) 58.00
        Cuba (7, 946pp.) 40.00
        Spain (4, 246pp.) 22.00
        Portugal (8, 368pp.) 42.00
        Philippines (4,501pp.) 23.00
            The complete set, 190.00   RDX   1692

Speed, Joshua Fry, 1814 (AP-1)--Reminiscences of
    Abraham Lincoln and Notes of a visit to Calif. ...
    Louisville, Ky., printed by J.P. Morton & Co., 1884.
    67p. 2.45 LoC   1693

Speed, Thomas, 1841 (KC-14)--Who fought the battle?
    Strength of the Union and Confederate forces compared...
    (Louisville, Ky., Press of F.G. Nunemacher, 1904).
    Cover-title. 31p. 3.95 LoC   1694

Speer, Daniel--Grund-richtiger ... jetzt wolvermehrter
unterricht der musicalischen kunst. Ulm, 1697.
3.75 UR   1695

Spelman, Henry (TOS-4)--Relation of Virginia, ... 1609.
London, printed for J.F. Hunnewell at the Chiswick
Press, 1872. 5.95 LoC   1696

Spence, James, 1816 (AP-1)--On the recognition of the
Southern Confederation. London, Richard Bentley,
1862. 48p. 2.45 LoC   1697

Spencer, Oliver M. (OV-A5)--Indian captivity; a true
narrative of the capture of Rev. O.M. Spencer,
by the Indians, in the neighborhood of Cincinnati.
New York, Carlton & Lanahan (pref. 1834). 160p.
3.66 LoC   1698

Spencer, Theodore--Death and Elizabethan tragedy; a
study of convention and opinion in the Elizabethan drama.
2.25 SM   1699

Spofford Fam.--A family record of the descendants of
John Spofford and Elizabeth, his wife, who settled at
Rowley in 1638. By Jeremiah Spofford. Haverhill,
Mass., 1851. 64p. 1.20 GML   1700

Spring, Gardiner (TOS-3)--Memoirs of the Rev. Samuel
J. Mills, late missionary to the South Western section of
the United States, ... New-York, New-York Evangelical
Missionary Soc., J. Seymour, printer, 1820. 5.95
LoC   1701

Stanton, Daniel (TOS-1)--A journal of the life, travels,
and gospel labours of a faithful minister of Jesus Christ,
... Philadelphia, printed and sold by Joseph Crukshank,
1772. 5.95 LoC   1702

Starke, Vivian A. (ACRL-106)--A check-list of Richmond,
Virginia imprints, 1853-1860. 1957. Thesis (M.S.
in L.S.), Catholic Univ. of America. 1.50 UR   1703

Stein, Evaleen (OV-A5)--One way to the woods. Boston,
Copeland & Day, 1897. 72p. 2.78 LoC   1704

Steinberg, Sheldon S. (PE-398)--Physical education in
the college program of general education. 1956.
Thesis (Ed.D.), Columbia Univ. 213p. 2.05 O   1705

Stephens, Alexander Hamilton (AP-1)--Secession condemned
in a southern convention. Manchester, Union & Emancipation Soc., 1861? 2p. 2.45 LoC   1706

Stephens, Thomas (TOS-4)--A brief account of the
causes that have retarded the progress of the colony
of Georgia, in America; ... London, printed in the
year 1743. 5.95 LoC   1707

Stephens, William (TOS-4)--A state of the province of
Georgia, attested upon oath in the court of Savannah,
Nov. 10, 1740. London, printed for W. Meadows,
1742. 5.95 LoC   1708

Stephenson, Edward A.--Milton's materials for Comus.
1.05 KU   1709

Stephenson, G. M.--Political history of public lands,
1840-62. 3.00 SM   1710

Stewart, William George Drummond, 7th bart. (P&R-2)--
Altowan: or, incidents of life and adventure in the
Rocky Mountains. ... 2v. 5.95 each   LoC   1711

Stiles, Joseph Clay (KC-9)--A letter of Alexander Campbell,
in reply to an article in the Millennial Harbinger.
Lexington, Ky., Lexington Intelligencer Print, 1838.
57p. 2.62 LoC   1712

--------(OV-5)--Modern reform examined; or, The
Union of North and South on the subject of slavery.
Philadelphia, J.B. Lippincott & Co., 1858. 310p.
5.40 LoC   1713

Stille, Charles Janeway, 1819 (AP-1)--How a free people
conduct a long war: a chapter from English history.
Philadelphia, Wm.S. & Alfred Martien, 1863. 40p.
2.45 LoC   1714

Stillingfleet (LR-E&W)--Ecclesiastical. 2v. (1702-04).
MMP   1715

Stillman, Annie Raymond (S-B4)--How they kept the faith, a tale of the Huguenots of Languedoc, by Grace Raymond (pseud.). London (etc.), T. Nelson & Sons, 1889. vi, 389p. 3.95 LoC   1716

Stockard, Henry Jerome (S-B3)--Fugitive lines. New York, G.P. Putnam's Sons, 1897. 93p. 3.25 LoC   1717

Stoddard, A.F. (AP-1)--Slavery or Freedom in America, or, The issue of the war. Glasgow, T. Murray & Son, 1863. 64p. 2.45 LoC   1718

Stoddard, Amos (TOS-3)--Sketches, historical and descriptive, of Louisiana. ...Philadelphia, pub. by Mathew Carey, A. Small, printer ... 1812. 5.95 LoC   1719

Stone, Barton Warren (TOS-2)--Biography ... written by himself, with additions and reflections, by Elder John Rogers. ... Cincinnati, pub. for the author by J.A. & U.P. James, 1847. 5.95 LoC   1720

Storrs, Hon. Augustus (P&R-1)--Answers of Augustus Storrs, Missouri, to certain queries upon ... trade and intercourse between Missouri and the internal provinces of Mexico, propounded by the Hon. Mr. Benton. Jan. 3, 1825. 5.95 LoC   1721

Stowe, Mrs. Harriet Elizabeth (Beecher), 1811 (AP-1)-- A reply to "The affectionate and Christian address of many thousands of women of Great Britain and Ireland, to their sisters the women of the U.S.A." London, S. Low, Son & Co., 1863. ...63p. 2.45 LoC   1722

Strachey, William (TOS-4)--The historie of travaile into Virginia Britannia; ... Now first ed. from the original ms., in the British Museum, by R.H.Major. ... London, printed for the Hakluyt Society, 1849. 5.95 LoC   1723

Strange news fromVirginia (TOS-1); being a full and true account of the life and death of Nathaniel Bacon, ... London, printed for Wm. Harris, ... 1677. 5.95 LoC   1724

Stranger, traveller, and merchant's guide through the
United States (TOS-2). Philadelphia, 1825. 5.95
LoC   1725

Stratton, Stephen T. (PSY-120)--Methods of grouping boys
nine years of age according to their level of aspiration
based on grip strength efforts. 1960. Thesis (M.S.),
Univ. of Oregon. 83p. 1.40 O   1726

Street, Richard Herbert (PE-424)--Measurement of
achievement in skiing. 1957. Thesis (M.S.), Univ.
of Utah. 118p. 1.40 O   1727

Strickland, W.P., ed. (MFM, also TOS-5?)--Peter
Cartwright, the backwoods preacher: an autobiography
of Peter Cartwright. 1858. 5.95 LoC   1728

Strindberg, August--Antibarbarus. Berlin, 1894
(Widmungsexemplar). Nr. 301-302. MK   1729

Stuart, Granville (P&R-1)--Montana as it is; being a general
description of its resources, ... to which is appended,
a complete dictionary of the Snake Language, and also
of the famous Chinnook Jargon, ... 5.95 LoC   1730

Stubbs, Sidney Thomas (PSY-89)--A study of the attitudes
of university freshmen male students toward athletes
and athletics. 1957. Thesis (M.A.), Ohio State Univ.
88p. 1.25 O   1731

Sullivan, Edward Robert (P&R-1)--Rambles and scrambles
in North and South America. 5.95 LoC   1732

Sumner, Charles, 1811 (AP-1)--Speech ... on the
Johnson-Clarendon treaty for the settlement of claims.
Delivered in the U.S. Senate (April 13, 1869). ...
Boston, Wright & Potter, printers, 1870. 69p. 2.45
LoC   1733

--------(AP-1)--Our foreign relations. New York,
Young Men's Republican Union, 1863. 80p. 2.45
LoC   1734

Sutcliff, Robert (TOS-4)--Travels in some parts of North
America, in the years 1804-06. York [Eng.] printed
by C. Peacock for W. Alexander, 1811 5.95 LoC   1735

Sutherland--The religious background of Swift's "A Tale of a Tub." 1.40 KU 1736

Swartz, Jean Marie (ACRL-107)--A check-list of Richmond, Virginia imprints, 1866 to 1870. 1955. Thesis (M.S. in L.S.), Catholic Univ. of America. 2.25 UR 1737

Swem, Earl Gregg, ed. (TOS-3)--Letters on the condition of Kentucky in 1825; ... New York City, printed by C.F. Heartman, 1916. 5.95 LoC 1738

Sylvestris (pseud.)--See Tucker, St. George.

T

Taggert, Mary C. (PE-399)--Construction and application of an instrument to measure outcomes of the physical education program as an integral part of early elementary education. 1957. Thesis (Ph.D.), New York Univ. 176p. 1.90 O 1739

Tailfer, Patrick (TOS-2)--A true and historical narrative of the colony of Georgia, in America, from the first settlement thereof until this present period: ... Charles Town, S. Car., printed by P. Timothy, for the authors, 1741. 5.95 LoC 1740

Tallmadge, Samuel (TOS-1)--Orderly books of the 4th New York regiment, 1778-1780, the 2d New York regiment, 1780-1783, by S. Tallmadge and others, with diaries of S. Tallmadge, 1780-1782, and John Barr, 1779-1782; prepared for publication by A.W. Lauber, ... Albany, The Univ. of the State of New York, 1932. 5.95 LoC 1741

Taney, Mary Florence (KC-10)--Kentucky pioneer women, Columbian poems and prose sketches. Cincinnati, Press of R. Clarke & Co., 1893. 5,99p. 2.63 LoC 1742

Tanner, Thomas, bp. of St. Asaph (BC-3)--Bibliotheca britannico-hibernica: sive, De scriptoribus, qui in Anglia, Scotia, et Hibernia ad saeculi XVII initium floruerunt, literarum ordine juxta familiarum nomina dispositis commentarius ... Praefixa est ... Davidis Wilkinsii Londini, excudit G. Bowyer, impensis Societatis ad literars promovendas institutae, 1748. 788p. 10.66 LoC   1743

Tartini, Giuseppe--Traite des agremens de la musique. Paris [1782] 1.00 UR   1744

Tatham, William (TOS-2)--An historical and practical essay on the culture and commerce of tobacco. London, printed for Vernor & Hood, 1800. 5.95 LoC1745

Taylor--The short stories of Jesse Stuart. 1.05 KU   1746

Taylor, Gerry Mailand (ACRL-115)--Vocational interests of male librarians in the United States. 1955. Thesis (M.L.S.), Univ. of Texas. 1.50 UR   1747

Taylor, James Wickes. Legislature of Minnesota (P&R-2)-- Northwest British America and its relations to the State of Minnesota. 5.95 LoC   1748

Taylor, Mary Virginia--The public library commission of Indiana. 1953. Thesis (M.A.), Univ. of Kentucky. 1.05 KU   1749

Taylor, William, 1821 (AP-1)--Cause and probable results of the Civil War in America. Facts for the people of Great Britain. London, Simkin, Marshall & Co., 1862. 32p. 2.45 LoC   1750

Tea Leaves - Being a collection of letters and documents relating to the shipment of tea to the American colonies in the year 1773, by the East India Tea Company. 2.00 SM   1751

        Temple, Launcelot, pseud.--See Armstrong, John

Testut, Charles (S-B3)--Le vieux Salomon; ou, Une famille d'esclaves au xixe siecle. Nouvelle-Orleans, 1872. 176p. 3.25 LoC   1752

Thackston, Frances Venable (ACRL-124)--The development
of cataloging in the libraries of Duke University and the
University of North Carolina. 1959. Thesis (M.S.
in L.S.), Univ. of North Carolina. 1.50 UR   1753

Theatre Arts. Vols. 1-8 (1916-1924). 28.00 C   1754

Thomas, C.A. [et al.]--Anhydrous aluminum chloride
in organic chemicals. 1941. ACS monograph no. 87.
29.70   MXT   1755

Thomas, David (TOS-3)--Travels through the western
country in ... 1816. ... Auburn (N.Y.), printed
by David Rumsey, 1819. 5.95   LoC   1756

Thomas, Davis, 1732 (KC-14)--The observer trying
the great reformation in this state, and proving it to
have been originally a work of divine power. Lexington,
printed by John Bradford (1802). ...43p. 3.95
LoC   1757

Thomas, Frederick William (OV-A5)--Autobiography ...
Baltimore, Gobright, Thorne & Co., 1852. 119p.
3.30   LoC   1758

--------(OV-A5)--The beechen tree. A tale, told in
rhyme. New York, Harper & Bros., 1844. 95p.
3.04   LoC   1759

--------(OV-A5)--Clinton Bradshaw; or, The adventures
of a lawyer. Philadelphia, Carey, Lea & Blanchard,
1835. 2v. v1, 4.78; v2, 3.60   LoC   1760

--------(OV-A5)--The emigrant; or, Reflections while
descending the Ohio. A poem. Cincinnati, A. Flash,
1833. 48p. 2.52   LoC   1761

--------(KC-9)--Sketches of character, and tales founded
on fact. Louisville, published at the office of the
Chronicle of Western Literature and Art, 1849. 117p.
3.28   LoC   1762

Thomas, I.--History of printing in America. 2v. 12.00
SM   1763

Thomas, Joseph (TOS-2)--The life of the Pilgrim, Joseph Thomas, ... Winchester, Va., J. Foster, printer, 1817. 5.95 LoC   1764

--------(TOS-4)--Poems, religious, moral and satirical, ... to which is prefixed ... life, travels ... Lebanon, O., Office of the Western Star, 1829. 5.95 LoC   1765

Thompson, Charles Lemuel (KC-8)--Times of refreshing. A history of American revivals from 1740 to 1877, with their philosophy and methods. Chicago, L.T. Palmer & Co. (etc. etc.), 1877. 483p. 7.30 LoC 1766

Thompson, Maurice (S-B3)--A fortnight of folly. New York, J.B. Alden, 1888. 4,140p. 3.25 LoC   1767

--------(S-B4)--The king of Honey Island. A novel. With illus. by H.M. Eaton. New York, R. Bonner's Sons, 1893. 7,34p. 3.95 LoC   1768

--------(S-B3)--Lincoln's grave. Cambridge & Chicago, Stone & Kimball, 1894. 48p. 3.25 LoC   1769

--------(S-B4)--A Tallahassee girl. Boston, J.R. Osgood & Co., 1882. 355p. 3.95 LoC   1770

Thompson, Melvin W. (PE-444)--Relationship of preseason physical testing and post season rank of selected high school football players. 1959. Thesis (M.S.), State College of Washington. 40p. 1.15 O   1771

Thorpe, T.B. (MFM)--The hive of the bee-hunter. 1854. 312p. 4.92 LoC   1772

--------(MFM)--Mysteries of the backwoods. 1846. 190p. 3.58 LoC   1773

Three centuries of English and American plays. Checklist. To subscribers to microprint edition of plays, no charge. RDX   1774

Thwaites, Reuben Gold--Early Western travels. proposed, 80.00 F   1775

Thurston, Samuel Royal (P&R-2)--Geographical statistics. Oregon, its climate, soil production, etc. 5.95 LoC 1776

Tiernan, Mrs. Frances Christine (Fisher) (S-B3)--
"The land of the sky;" or, Adventures in mountain
byways. By Christian Reid (pseud.). New York,
D. Appleton & Co., 1876. 3,130p. 3.25 LoC 1777

Tilghman, Oswald--See Harrison, Samuel Alexander

Todd, G. B.--Life and letters of Joel Barlow. 2.75
SM 1778

Tomlins (LR-E&W)--Election. 1v. (1689-1795).
MMP 1779

Tonty, Henri de (TOS-4)--"Memorial sent in 1693, on the
discovery of the Mississippi and the neighboring nations
by M. de la Salle, from the year 1678 to the time of
his death, and by the Sieur de Tonty to the year 1691, "
Early narratives of the Northwest, 1634-1699. Original
narratives of early American history, ed. by L.P.
Kellogg. New York, Charles Scribner's Sons, 1917.
5.95 LoC 1780

--------(TOS-1)--"Relation of Henri de Tonty, entreprises
de M. de la Salle, de 1678 à 1683, " ... trans. by
M.B. Anderson. Chicago, The Caxton Club, 1898.
5.95 LoC 1781

Torrey Botanical Club Bulletin. Vols. 1-23 (1870-
1896). 67.50 C 1782

Tower, Philo (KC-9)--Slavery unmasked: being a truthful
narrative of three years' residence and journeying
in eleven Southern states: to which is added the invasion
of Kansas, including the last chapter of her wrongs.
Rochester, E. Darrow & Brothers, 1856. 432p. 6.74
LoC 1783

Townsend, John (AP-1)--The southern states, their
present peril and their certain remedy. ... Charleston,
printed by E.C. Councell, 1850. 31p. 2.45 LoC 1784

Tracy, Ebenezer Carter (TOS-2)--Memoir of the life of
Jeremiah Evarts ... Boston, Crocker & Brewster,
1845. 5.95 LoC 1785

Tranchepain, Marie de St. Augustin (TOS-2)--Relation du
voyage prèmieres   Ursulines à la Nouvelle Orleans et
de leur établissement en cette ville. ...New York,
Cramoisy Press of J.G. Shea, 1859. 5.95 LoC   1786

Travels in the Old South. Group 1. Per vol., as a group,
4.00 (116 vols.) LoC   1787
The titles in this series are:

    Adair, J.--History of the American Indians ...
    Allemagne, d'--Nouvelles du Scioto, ...
    Alsop, G.--Character of the province of Mary-land,
    Alter und verbesserter Schreib-Kalender, ...
    Ashe, T.--Travels in America, ...
    Aston, A.--The fool's opera; ...
    Badin, S.T.--Origine et progres de la mission du
       Kentucky, ...
    Barry, T.--... Captivity among the Monsipi
       Indians ...
    Benavides, A.--Memorial qve fray Ivan de Santander
    Birkbeck, M.--Notes on a journey in America...
    Bolton, H.E.--Arrendondo's historical proof of
       Spain's title to Georgia.
    Bonrepos, C.--Description du Mississippi, ...
    Borden, W.--Address to the Inhabitants of North
       Carolina ...
    Brackenridge, H.M. (also OV-A2; P&R-1)--Views
       of Louisiana; ...
    Bradbury, J. (also TOS-1)--Travels in the interior
       of America, ...
    Brion de la Tour, L.--Almanach intéressant dans
       les circonstances presentes.
    Brockway, T.--The European traveller in America.
    Bullock, W.--Virginia impartially examined, ...
    Burnyeat, J.--The truth exalted ...
    Byrd, W.--Journey to the land of Eden in the year
       1733.
    Byrd, W.--Progress to the mines, in the year 1732.
    Byrd, W.--History of the dividing line, run in the
       year 1728.
    Cabeza de Vaca, A.-- Journey ... from Florida to
       the Pacific, ...
    Cartwright, P.--Autobiography ...
    Castiglioni, L.--Viaggio negli Stati Uniti dell'
       America Settentrionale, ...

Champigny, J.--La Louisiane ensanglantée, ...
Charlevoix, P.F.---Histoire et description
generale de la Nouvelle France, ...
Charlevoix, P.F.--Journal d'un voyage fait ...
dans l'Amérique Septentrionale, ...
Chetwood, W.R.--The voyages, dangerous adven-
tures, and imminent escapes of Capt. Richard
Falconer; ...
Christie, T.--A description of Georgia, ...
Churchman, J.--Account of gospel labours, and
Christian experiences ...
Clarke, G.--Voyage to America.
Coke, T.--Extracts of the journals ...
A compendious description of the thirteen colonies,
Crafford, J.--New account of Carolina ...
Croghan, G.--Journal, ...
Cutler, J. (also OV-A4; P&R-1)--Topographical
description of the state of Ohio, ...
D'Arusmont, F.W.--Views of society and manners
in America; ...
De La Warr, T.W.--The relation of Lord De-La-
Warre, ...
Descrizione geografica di parte dell' America
Settentrionale.
Duden, G.--Bericht über eine Reise nach den
westlichen Staaten Nordamerika's...
Du Pratz, A.S.--Histoire de la Louisiane, ...
Du Ru, P.--Journal ...
Farmer, R.--Letters from Illinois, ...
Fraser, A.--Report on the Illinois country.
Flower, R.--Letters from Lexington and the
Illinois, ...
Forest, M.--Travels through America.
French, B.F.--Historical collections of Louisiana,
Freytas, N.--The expedition of Don Diego Dionisio
de Peñalosa ...
Furlong, L.--The American coast pilot; ...
Geschichte und handlung der französischen
pflanzstadte in Nord-amerika.
Green, W.--The sufferings of W. Green; ...
Guthrie, W.--New geographical, historical,
and commercial grammar, ...
Hall, F.--Importance of the British plantations in
America ...
Hamilton, H.--Report...

Hammond, J. --Hammond versus Heamans.
Hare, J. T. --Life and dying confession...
Harris, W. T. --Remarks made during a tour through
    the United States of America, ...
Hewatt, A. --Historical account of the colonies of
    South Carolina and Georgia. ...
Hilton, W. --Discovery lately made on the coast
    of Florida, ...
Hulme, T. --Journal, ...
Johnston, G. --Carolina Chronicle; ...
Jones, C. --Description of Weir's cave, ...
Joutel, H. --Journal historique ...
Kelly, S. --An eighteenth century Seaman, ...
Kimber, E. --...Journal of a late expedition to the
    gates of St. Augustine, ...
Lafayette, M. J. --Memoirs, correspondence, and
    manuscripts.
La Harpe, B. --Journal historique ...
Landolphe, J. F. --Memoires ...
Letters on emigration
Makemie, F. --Plain and friendly persuasive to the
    inhabitants of Virginia and Maryland...
Marquette, J. --Voyage et découverte de quelque
    pays et nations de l'Amérique Septentrionale, ...
Mühlenberg, H. M. --...Selbstbiographie,...
Paine, R. --Life and times of Wm. M'Kendree, ...
Palisot de Beauvois, A. M. --Insectes recuellis
    en Afrique et en Amerique, ...
Pena y Reyes, J. A. --Derrotero de la expedicion
    en la provincia de los Texas, ...
Penicaut, J. --Relation ou annales veritables...dans
    le pays de la Louisiane ...
Pinckney, Mrs. E. --Journal and letters.
Popp, S. --Journal, ...
Purviance, L. --Biography of the elder David
    Purviance, ...
Reed, I. --The Christian traveller.
Reise von Hamburg nach Philadelphia.
Revel, J. --...Felon's sorrowful account of his
    fouteen years transportation at Virginia...
Richardson, J. --Account of the life of J. Richardson
Schmidt, F. --Versuch über den politischen Zustand
    der Vereinigten Staaten von Nord-Amerika ...
Schoolcraft, H. R. --The Indian in his wigwam, ...
Scott, J. --Journal ...

Scotus Americanus, pseud.--Informations concerning
the province of North Carolina, ...
Smith, J.--Account of the remarkable occurrences
during his captivity with the Indians, ...
Smith, J.--A map of Virginia.
Stanton, D.--Journal ...
Strange news from Virginia; ...
Tallmadge, S.--Orderly books of the 4th New York
regiment, ...
Tonty, H.--"Relation..."
Twining, T.--Travels in India, ... with a visit
to the United States.
Varlo, C.--Nature display'd, ...
Velasco, J.I.--Triaca producida de un veneno.
Wesley, J.--Extract of ... journal ...
Whitaker, A.--Good newes from Virginia.
White, A.--Relation of Maryland; ...
Wilson, S.--Account of the Province of Carolina...
Wilson, T.--Brief journal ...
Yonge, F.--Narrative of the Proceedings of the
people of South-Carolina, ...
Yonge, F.--View of the trade of South-Carolina, ...

Travels in the Old South. Group 2. Per vol., as a group,
approx. 4.00 (123 vols.)   LoC   1788
The titles in this series are:

The American gazetteer.
Amerika, in alle zyne byzonderheden beschouwd, ...
Audubon, J.J.--Journal ... trip to New Orleans.
Bartram, W.--... Travels through North and South
Carolina, ...
Beltrami, G.C.--Pilgrimage in Europe and America,
Bingley, W.--Travels in North America, ...
Blane, W.N.--Excursion through the United States
and Canada ...
Blowe, D.--Geographical, historical, commercial,
and agricultural view of the United States of
America; ...
Bossu, J.B.--Nouveau voyages aux Indies occiden-
tales; ...
Bulow, D.--Der freistaat von Nordamerika in
seinem neusten zustand, ...
Butel-Dumont, G.M.--Histoire et commerce des
colonies angloises, ...

Carver, J. --The new universal traveller; ...

Chalmers, L. --An account of the weather and
diseases of South-Carolina.

Clark, G.R. --Memoir.

Coleraine, G. H. --Life, adventures and opinions
of Col. George Hanger.

A concise historical account of all the British
colonies in North-America, ...

Cuming, F. --Sketches of a tour to the western
country, ...

Darby, W. --A new gazetteer of the United States
of America ...

Dearborn, H. --Revolutionary war journals.

A detail of some particular services performed in
America, ...

Du Roi, A.W. --Journal ...

Evans, E. --A pedestrious tour, ...

Extrait du journal d'un officier de la marine ...

Fenning, D. --A new system of geography; .. .

Flint, T. --Recollections ... journeyings in the
valley of the Mississippi, ...

Forman, S. --Journey down the Ohio and Mississippi

Franklin, J. --Philosophical and political history
of the thirteen United States of America.

Gall, L. --Meine Auswanderung nach den Vereinigten-
Staaten ...

Gano, J. --Biographical memoirs ...

Graham, S. --Memoir.

Gravier, J. --Lettre ... sur les affaires de la
Louisiane.

Gravier, J. --...Journal du voyage ... depuis le
pays de Illinois ...

Gray, J. --Life of Joseph Bishop, ...

Griffith, J. --Journal ...

Gronovius, J.F. --Flora virginica, ...

Hall, F. --Travels in Canada, and in the United States,

Harrison, S.A. --Memoir of Lt. Col. Tench
Tilghman, ...

Hecke, J.V. --Reise durch die Vereinigten Staaten...

Hewett, D. --The American traveller; ...

Holcombe, H. --The First Fruits in a series of
letters.

Hutchins, T. --Historical narrative and topographical description of Louisiana and West-Florida, ...

Kingdom, W. --America and the British colonies.

Knight, H.D.--Letters from the South and West.
Lambert, J.--Travels through lower Canada, and
the United States of North America, ...
Laval, A.J.--Voyage de la Louisiane, ...
Mackenzie, E.--Historical, topographical, and
descriptive view of the United States of America,
Mason, J.--Extracts from a diary ... of a journey
from Boston to Savannah ...
Melish, J.--Description of the roads in the United
States.
Melish, J.--Geographical description of the United
States, ...
Melish, J.--Information and advice to emigrants
to the United States: ...
Melish, J.--Travels through the United States of
America ...
Michaux, F.A.--Voyage à l'ouest des mont
Alléghanys, ...
Miller, A.--New States and territories, ...
Mills, S.J.--Missionary tour...west of the
Allegany Mountains; ...
Mitchell, J.--Present state of Great Britain and
North America, ...
Montlezun, B.--Voyage fait ... de New-York a
la Nouvelles Orleans, ...
Neilson, P.--...Six years' residence in the United
States ...
The North-American and the West-Indian gazetteer.
Ogden, G.W.--Letters from the west; ...
Olin, S.--Life and letters.
Pagès, P.M.--Voyages autour du monde, ...
Palmer, J.--Journal of travels in the United States
of America; ...
Pearse, J.--Narrative of the life ...
Priest, W.--Travels in the United States of America;
The Rambler, or a tour through Virginia, ...
Ramsay, D.--Sketch of the soil, climate, weather,
and diseases of South-Carolina, ...
Reynolds, J.--My Own Times, ...
Ritson, Mrs. A.--Poetical picture of America, ...
Schoolcraft, H.R.--Journal of a tour into the
interior of Missouri and Arkansaw, ...
Schöpf, J.D.--Reise durch einige der mittlern und
Südlichen Vereinigten nordamerikanischen
Staaten ...

Seward, W.--Journal of a voyage from Savannah
    to Philadelphia, ...
Seymour, W.--Journal of the southern expedition, ...
Sharan, J.--Adventures ...
Stone, B.W.--Biography ... written by himself.
Stranger, traveller, and merchant's guide through
    the United States.
Smyth, J.F.--A tour in the United States of America:
Tailfer, P.--...Narrative of the colony of Georgia, ...
Tatham, W.--...Essay on the culture and commerce
    of tobacco.
Thomas, J.--Life of the Pilgrim, ...
Tracy, E.C.--Memoir of the life of Jeremiah
    Evarts...
Tranchepain, M.--Relation du voyage premières
    Ursulines à la Nouvelle Orleans ...
Tucker, G.--Letters from Virginia, ...
Walcot, J.--The new Pilgrim's progress;...
Waldo, S.P.--Memoirs of Andrew Jackson, ...
Walker, T.--Journal of an exploration in the ...
    year 1750.
Warden, D.B.--Statistical, political, and historical
    account of the United States ...
Washington, G.--Diaries ...1748-1799.
Young, J.--Autobiography of a Pioneer.

Travels in the Old South. Group 3. Per vol., as a group,
    approx. 4.00 (112 vols.) LoC   1789
The titles in this series are:

Asbury, F.--Journal ...
Bacon, Mrs. L.--Journal ...
Baily, F.--Journal of a tour in unsettled parts of
    North America, ...
Bayard, F.M.--Voyage dans l'interiéur des
    Etats-Unis, ...
Beaujour, L.A.--Apercu des Etats-Unis, ...
Bernard, J.--Retrospections of America, ...
Berquin-Duvallon--Vue de la colonie espagnole du
    Mississippi, ...
Brissot de Warville, J.P.--Nouveau voyage dans
    les Etats-Unis ...
Brooks, J.--Life and times ...
Brown, S.R.--The western gazetteer; ...

Beuchler, J.U.--Land--und Seereisen eines
   St. Gallischen Kantonsburgers nach Nord-amerika
Candler, I.--Summary view of America: ...
Claiborne, J.F.--Life and times of Gen. Sam Dale,
Coffin, L.--Reminiscences ...
Cooper, T.--Some information respecting America,
Dana, E.--Geographical sketches on the western
   country: ...
Darby, W.--Emigrant's guide to the western and
   southwestern states and territories ...
Darby, W.--View of the United States, ...
Davis, J.--Travels ... in the United States of
   America; ...
Descourtilz, M.E.--Voyages d'un Naturaliste, ...
Döhla, J.C.--Tagebuch eines Bayreuther soldaten,
Dörnberg, K.L.--Tagebuchblätter eines hessischen
   offiziers ...
Douglass, W.--Summary ... of the British
   settlements in North America; ...
Dow, L.--History of Cosmopolite; ...
Drayton, J.--View of South-Carolina, ...
Durand, of Dauphiné -- Voyages d'un Francois,
   exilé pour la religion, ...
Ellicott, A.--Journal ...
The Emigrant's guide, ...
Entick, J.--Present state of the British empire...
Esquisse intéressant du Tableau fidele des causes
   qui ont occasioné les révolutions actuelles de
   l'Amérique Septentrionale, ...
Ewell, J.D.--Life of Rev. Wm. Keele, ...
Faux, W.--Memorable days in America.
Filson, J.--Discovery, settlement and present state
   of Kentucke; ...
Flint, J.--Letters from America, ...
Forbes, J.G.--Sketches ... of the Floridas; ...
Hager, H.--Warhaffte Nachricht von einer hoch-
   teutschen evangelischen colonie zu Germantown,...
Harriott, J.--Struggles through life, ...
Harris, T.M.--Journal of a tour ... northwest of the
   Alleghany mountains; ...
History of North America ...
Hodgson, A.--Letters from North America, ...
Hodgson, A.--Remarks during a journey through
   North America...
Holmes, I.--Account of the United States of America,

Hoskins, J.--...Voyage from England, to the
    United States ...
Imlay, G.--Topographical description of the
    western territory of North America; ...
Janson, C.W.--The Stranger in America.
Jaquith, J.--...Different manners and customs...
    of the United States of America, ...
Ker, H.--Travels through the western interior
    of the United States, ...
La Rochefoucauld-Liancourt--Voyage dans les
    Etats-Unis d'Amerique, ...
Marrant, J.--Narrative of the Lord's wonderful
    dealings ...
May, J.--Journal and letters ...
Melish, J.--Traveller's directory through the
    United States.
Middleton, C.T.--New and complete system of
    geography.
Moreau de Saint-Mery, M.L.--Voyage aux Etats-
    Unis de l'Amérique, ...
N., J.C.--Naauwkeurige Beschryving van Noord-
    America ...
A new voyage to Georgia.
Nolte, V.--Fifty years in both hemispheres; ...
Nouvelle relation de la Caroline, ...
Nuttall, T.--Journal of travels into theArkansas
    Territory, ...
Oehler, A.--Life, adventures and unparalleled
    sufferings ...
Osborn, C.--Journal ...
Page, C.G.--Darstellung der bürgerlichen
    Verhältnisse in den Freistaaten von Nord-Amerika;
Palairet, J.--Concise description of the English
    and French possessions in North America, ...
Pope, J.--Tour through the southern and western
    territories ...
Rich, R.--Nevves from Virginia.
Riedesel, F.C.--Auszuge aus den briefen und
    papieren ...
Schermerhorn, J.F.--Correct view of ... the
    United States which lies west of the Allegany
    mountains, ...
Schoolcraft, H.R.--Travels in the central portion of
    the Mississippi valley; ...

Schoolcraft, H.R.--View of the lead mines of
  Missouri.
Schultz, C.--Travels...
Scott, J.--The United States gazetteer: ...
Shaw, J.--United States directory for the use of
  travellers and merchants.
Smith, D.--Journal ...
Spring, G.--Memoirs of the Rev. Samuel J. Mills,
Stoddard, A.--Sketches, ... of Louisiana.
Swem, E.G.--Letters on the condition of Kentucky
  in 1825.
Thomas, D.--Travels through the western country...
Vallette Laudun, de--Journal d'un voyage à la
  Louisiane, ...
Vigne, G.T.--Six months in America.
Washington, G.--Journal ...
Wilson, A.--American ornithology.
Woods, J.--Two years' residence ... in the
  Illinois country.
Young, W.A.--History of North and South America.

Travels in the Old South. Group 4. Per vol., as a group,
  approx. 4.00 (119 vols.) LoC   1790
The titles in this series are:

Archdale, J.--New description of... Carolina
Arricivita, J.D.--Crónica seráfica y apostolica ...
  en la Nueva Espana ...
Ashe, T.--Carolina; ...
Attmore, W.--Journal of a tour to North Carolina.
Beknopte en zakelyke der voornaamste engelsche
  volkplantingen, ...
Bolzius, J.M.--Extract of the journals ...
Bownas, S.--Account of the life, travels and Christian
  experiences.
Bray, T.--Apostolick charity, ...
Bray, T.--Memorial, representing the present
  state of religion on the continent of North America.
Brickell, J.--Natural history of North-Carolina.
Das brittische reich in America, ...
Brown, T.--Memoirs ...
Carey, M.--Carey's American pocket atlas.
Carolina described more fully than heretofore ...
Castelman, R.--Voyage, shipwreck and miraculous
  preservation ...

Chalkley, T.--Journal of ... life, travels and
   Christian experiences ...
Champigny, J.--Present state of ... Louisiana, ...
Cooke, E.--Sotweed redivivus.
Cooke, E.--The Sot-weed factor.
Cornelius, E.--Memoir ...
Cresswell, N.--Journal ...
Crevecoeur, M.G.--Letters from an American
   farmer.
Cumings, S.--The Western pilot, ...
Darby, W.--Geographical description of ...
   Louisiana.
Denny, E.--Military journal ...
Dickinson, J.--Gods protecting providence, ...
Dow, Mrs. P.--Vicissitudes exemplified; ...
Dumas, M.--Memoirs of his own time.
Edmundson, W.--Journal of the life, travels and
   sufferings ...
Espy, J.M. (also KC-8)--Memorandums of a tour
   ... in the states of Ohio ...
Fanning, D.--Narrative ...
Feltman, W.--Journal ...
Flower, G.--The English settlement in Edwards
   county, Illinois.
Fontaine, J.--Memoirs of a Huguenot Family.
Garrettson, F.--Experience and travels.
Gilpin, T.--Exiles in Virginia; ...
Gist, C.--Journal ...
Glen, J.--Description of South Carolina.
Glover, T.--Account of Virginia, ...
Goldsmith, J.?--Present state of the British empire.
Grantham, T.--...Some memorable actions,
   particularly in Virginia.
Hall, J.--History of the Mississippi territory.
Hamor, R., the younger--Trve discovrse of the
   present state of Virginia, ...
Hartridge, W.C.--Letters of Robert Mackay.
Hartwell, H.--Present state of Virginia, ...
Hennepin, L.--Description de la Louisiane, ...
Holme, B.--...Epistles and works...
An impartial enquiry into the right of the French king
   to the territory west of the great river Mississippi,
J.R.--The Port-folio;...
Jefferson, T.--Notes on the state of Virginia; ...
Johnson, R.--New life of Virginia: ...

Johnston, E.--Recollections of a Georgia loyalist.
Jones, H.--Present state of Virginia.
Keith, G.--Journal of travels from New-Hampshire
    to Caratuck, ...
Lade, R.--Voyages...
Laudonnière, R.G.--L'histoire notable de la
    Floride ...
Lawson, J.--New voyage to Carolina; ...
Lederer, J.--Discoveries ... in three several
    marches from Virginia, ...
Levasseur, A.--Lafayette en Amerique, ...
Lorain, J.--Hints to emigrants, ...
Martyn, B.--Impartial enquiry into the...province
    of Georgia.
Mead, C.--Mississippian scenery; a poem.
Melish, J.--Statistical account of the United States.
Mifflin, B.--Journal ... record of a tour from
    Philadelphia to Delaware and Maryland.
Milligen, G.--Short description of the province of
    South-Carolina.
Montule, E.--Voyage en Amerique ...
Moore, F.--Voyage to Georgia; ...
Moré, C.A.--Mémoires ...
Murray, J.--Letters of J. Murray, loyalist.
Operations of the French fleet under Count de Grasse
    in 1781-2.
Pickering, J.--Emigration, or no emigration.
Pratt, W.--Journal ...
Reck, P.--Extract of Journals ...
Relation de la Louisianne ou Mississippi.
Relation of the successfulle beginnings of Lord
    Baltemore's Plantation in Mary-land.
Revel, G.J.--Journal particulier d'une campagne
    aux Indes Occidentales...
Rivera, P.--Diario y Derrotero de lo caminado, ...
Rochambeau, J.B.--Memoires militaires, histori-
    ques et politiques ...
Rochefort, C.--Histoire naturelle et morale des
    iles Antilles de l'Amérique.
Rochefort, C.--Recit de l'estat present des celebres
    colonies ...
Salmon, T.--The universal traveller; ...
Sargent, W.--History of an expedition against
    Fort Du Quesne ...

Saugrain de Vigni, A.F.--L'Odysée Américaine
d'une famille francaise.
Smith, J.--...Occurrences and accidents of
noate as hath hapned in Virginia ...
Smith, S.--Memoirs ...
Smith, W.L.--Journal ...
Some considerations on the consequences of the
French settling colonies on the Mississippi, ...
Spelman, H.--Relation of Virginia, ...
Stephens, T.--Brief account of the ... colony of
Georgia, ...
Stephens, W.--State of the province of Georgia, ...
Strachey, W.--Historie of travaile into Virginia
Britannia.
Sutcliff, R.--Travels in some parts of North
America, ...
Thomas, J.--Poems, religious, moral and
satirical, ...
Tonty, H.--"Memorial ... on the discovery of the
Mississippi..."
Uhlendorf, B.A.--Siege of Charleston; ...
Uring, N.--...Voyages and travels ...
Washington, G.--Journal of my journey over the
mountains; ...
Waterhouse, E.--Declaration of ...affaires in
Virginia.
Wesley, C.--Journal ...
Whitefield, G.--Works ...
Wild, E.--Journal ...
Wilhelm, P.--Erste Reise nach dem nördlichen
Amerika ...
Williams, W.--Journal of the life, travels and
gospel labours, ...
Woolman, J.--Journal of the life, gospel labours,...
Young, A.--Observations on the present state of
the waste lands of Great Britain.

Travels in the Old South. Group 5. in prep LoC 1791

Treille, A. & A. Meyer--Solution d'un grand probleme.
La navigation aérienne. Noyon (Oise), 1852.
Nr. 201. MK 1792

Triplett, Thomas (KC-11)--To the public (n.p.), 1832.
31p. 2.50 LoC 1793

Tripplett, Frank (MFM)--Conquering the wilderness.
  1883. 716p. 9.37 LoC   1794

Tristram's Consistory Judgements (LR-E&W)--Ecclesiasti-
  cal. 1v. (1872-90) MMP   1795

Tryon, R.M.--Household manufactures in the U.S.,
  1649-1860. 2.75 SM   1796

Tucker, George--Balcombe, a novel. 3.60 SM   1797

Tucker, George, supposed author (TOS-2)--Letters from
  Virginia, trans. from the French. ... Baltimore,
  pub. by Fielding Lucas, Jr., J. Robinson, printer,
  1816. 5.95 LoC   1798

Tucker, Nathaniel Beverly (S-B3)--Prescience. Speech
  delivered by Hon. Beverly Tucker, of Virginia; in the
  Southern convention, held at Nashville, Tenn., April
  13th, 1850. Richmond, Va., West & Johnson, 1862.
  38p. 3.25 LoC   1799

Tucker, St. George (S-B3)--Reflections on the cession of
  Louisiana to the United States. By Sylvestris (pseud.).
  Washington City, printed by Samuel Harrison Smith,
  1803. 27p. 3.25 LoC   1800

Tufts, James (P&R-1)--A tract descriptive of Montana
  Territory; with a sketch of its mineral and agricultural
  resources. 5.95 LoC   1801

Turner, Margery Jean (PSY-90)--An evaluation of the
  physical education program for its educative potential
  for democratic leadership development in college women.
  1957. Thesis (Ed.D.), New York Univ. 153p. 1.50
  O   1802

Turner, William--Sound anatomiz'd, in a philosophical
  essay on musick. London, 1724. 1.50 UR   1803

Turner, William, d. 1568 (HS-1)--A new herball.
London, Imprinted by S. Mierdman, 1551-62. 2v.
in 1. Illus. Vols. 2 has title: The seconde parte of
Uilliam Turners herball ... Here unto is ioyned also
a booke of the bath of Baeth in Englande and of the
vertues of the same wyth diuerse other bathes moste holsum
and effectuall both in Almany and Englande. Collen,
Imprinted by A. Birckman, 1562. 8.50 LoC   1804

Tuttle, Charles Richard, 1848 (KC-14)--History of the
border wars of two centuries, embracing a narrative
of the wars with the Indians from 1750 to 1874.
Chicago, C.A. Wall & Co., 1874. 608p. 3.95 LoC 1805

Twining, Thomas (TOS-1)--Travels in India a hundred
years ago, with a visit to the United States; ...ed. by
W.H.G. Twining, ... London, J.L. Osgood, McIlwaine
& Co., 1893. 5.95   LoC   1806

Tyrwhitt (LR-E&W)--Exchequer. 5v. (1830-35). MMP1807

Tyrwhitt & Granger (LR-E&W)--Exchequer. 1v. (1835-
36). MMP   1808

U

Udell, John (P&R-1)--Incidents of travel to California,
across the great plains; together with the return trips
through Central America and Jamaica; ... 5.95
LoC   1809

Uhlendorf, Bernhard A., ed. & trans. (TOS-4)--The siege
of Charleston, with an account of the province of South
Carolina; diaries and letters of Hessian officers from
the von Jungkenn Papers in the Wm. L. Clements
Library. ... Ann Arbor, Mich., Univ. of Michigan
Press, 1938.   5.95   LoC   1810

United Nations Current Publications to date. Annual subs.,
300.00 per year RDX   1811

United Nations Documents and Official Records (available
in separate units):
General Assembly: 1946-1953 - 950.00
                   1954-1956 - 310.00
                   1957   - 110.00
                   1958   - 110.00
Security Council: 1946-1953 - 400.00
                   1954-1956 -   63.00
                   1957   -   30.00
                   1958   -   30.00
Economic &
  Social Council: 1946-1953 - 1400.00
                   1954-1956 - 500.00
                   1957   - 175.00
                   1958   - 175.00
Trusteeship
  Council: 1946-1953 - 600.00
                   1954-1956 - 400.00
                   1957   - 125.00
                   1958   - 125.00
Disarmament Comm. & A.E.C. Comm: 1946-1953 -
    125.00
Disarmament Comm: 1954-1958   -   100.00 RDX 1812

U.S. Army (AP-1)--Report of Lt. Gen. U.S. Grant of
the armies of the United States--1864-65.   Washington,
D.C. 1865.   44p. 2.45 LoC   1813

U.S. Bureau of Mines--"Production and distribution of
ferrous and non-ferrous metals." 100.00 per year
RDX   1814

United States Chemical Patents (complete texts): 1958-
337.49; 1959 - 376.48; 1960 - 326.82; current
subs., 26cents per side GML   1815

U.S. "Federal Register." 1958 - 65.52; 1959 - 61.51;
1960 - price not available; current subs., 21 cents
per side   GML   1816

U.S. Fish Commission. Bulletin. Vols. VII and XX
AmG   1817

U.S. Government Depository Publications. Annual subs.,
3000.00 RDX (also available in departmental units) 1818

U.S. Government (Non-Depository) Publications.
Annual subs., 1800.00 RDX (also available in
departmental units)   1819

U.S. Government Publications. Congressional Hearings
and Committee Prints. Ed. with an index by Mrs.
D.I. Rossi and J. Rosenthal. 650.00 per year RDX1820

U.S. Government Publications. Federal Register.
1956- to date (with index) 60.00 per year RDX   1821

U.S. Government Publications. Joint Publications
Research Service. Translations ... approx. 2000
publications annually, estimated 250.00 per year
RDX   1822

U.S. Government Publications for Law Libraries:
  1. Hearings. Senate & House Judiciary Committees
     140.00 per year
  2. Current Serial Set (House & Senate documents &
     reports) 420.00 per year
  3. Congressional Record with appendix 100.00 per
     year; 50.00 per sess.
  4. Senate and House bills   350.00 per year
  5. Federal Register with index 60.00 per year
  6. Administrative decisions approx. 125.00 per year
RDX   1823

U.S. Patent Office "Official Gazette." 1958 - 120.35;
1959 - 140.40; 1960 - 132.09; current subs., 21 cents
per side GML   1824

U.S. Serial Set (Each group available separately:
  Group 8. Serial nos. 430-468 (28th Cong. 1843-1845)
     150.00
  Group 9. Serial nos. 469-501 (29th Cong. 1845-1847)
     125.00
  Group 10. Serial nos. 502-546 (30th Cong. 1847-1849)
     160.00
  Group 11. Serial nos. 547-606 (31st Cong. 1849-1851)
     155.00
  Group 12. Serial nos. 607-687 (32nd Cong. 1851-1853)
     225.00
  RDX   1825

U.S. Superintendent of Documents--Catalogue of the public
    documents. Vols. 1-15 (1896-1921), 180.00 C   1826

U.S. Supreme Court Records & Briefs (full opinion
    cases) - October, 1957 term, 254.75 B   1827

U.S. Supreme Court Records & Briefs. Cert. Den. and
    Per Curiam cases. Starting with Oct. 1956 term -
    complete; Oct. 1957 - in prep B   1828

Umphraville, Angus (OV-A5)--The siege of Baltimore, and
    the Battle of La Tranche; with other original poems.
    Baltimore, Printed by Schaeffer & Maund, 1817.
    144p. 3.57 LoC   1829

Upham, Charles Wentworth (P&R-1)--Life explorations
    and public services of John Charles Fremont. 5.95
    LoC   1830

Uring, Nathaniel (TOS-4)--A history of the voyages and
    travels of Capt. Nathaniel Uring. ... London, J.
    Peele, 1726. 5.95 LoC   1831

                          V

Vaillancour, Richard Lee (PH-56)--Evaluation of the
    physique, development level, and basal metabolism of
    two hundred selected individuals by the application of
    the Wetzel Grid technique. 1958. Thesis (M.Ed.),
    Oregon State College. 46p. 1.05 O   1832

Vallette Laudun, de (TOS-3)--Journal d'un voyage à la
    Louisiane, fait en 1720. ... A la Haye, et se trouve a
    Paris, Chez Musier, fils, & Fournier, 1768. 5.95
    LoC   1833

Van Buren, A. de Puy (MFM)--Jottings of a year's sojourn
    in the South. 1859. 320p. 5.01 LoC   1834

                        217

Van Huss, Wayne Daniel (PH-62)--The relationship of
selected tests with energy metabolism and swimming
performance. 1953. Thesis (Ph.D.), Univ. of
Illinois. 156p. 1.65 O   1835

Van Tiem, John E. (ACRL-109)--The theatre collection
of the New York Public Library. 1957. Thesis
(M.S. in L.S.), Western Reserve Univ.   .75 UR 1836

Varlo, Charles (TOS-1)--Nature display'd, a new work.
...3rd ed. London, printed for the editor, 1793.
5.95 LoC   1837

Velasco, José Ignacio de Toca (TOS-1)--Triaca producida
de un veneno. ... Poema, que dedica a Dona Isabel
Fernesio. Madrid, J. Sanchez, 1734. 5.95 LoC 1838

Veliz, Dorothy Benson de--Four literary manifestations
of the concept of Christ-like perfection. .70 KU 1839

Venable, W.H. (MFM, also OV-A3)--Beginnings of
literary culture in the Ohio Valley. 1891. 4.31
LoC   1840

Victor, William B. (KC-14)--Life and events. Cincinnati,
Applegate & Co., 1859. ...232p. 3.95 LoC   1841

Vigne, Godfrey Thomas (TOS-3)--Six months in America.
London, Wittaker, Treacher & Co., 1832. 2v.
5.95 each LoC   1842

Vincent, Robert Henry (PSY-91)--The influence of inter-
polated physical activity on mental work and achievement.
1954. Thesis (M.A.), Univ. of California. 20p.
1.05 O   1843

Voisard, Paul Peter (PSY-102)--A study of the relationship
between body build and motor educability of elementary
school boys, ages 10-13. 1954. Thesis (M.S.),
Univ. of Illinois. 98p. 1.40 O   1844

W

Waddel, John Newton (S-B4)--Memorials of academic life;
being an historical sketch of the Waddel family, identi-
fied through three generations with the history of the
higher education in the South and Southwest. Richmond,
Va., Presbyterian Committee of Publication, 1891.
583p. 3.95 LoC   1845

Wagner, Henry Raup--The Plains and the Rockies ...
rev. & extended by Charles L. Camp--See Series
entries: Plains and the Rockies or individual
entries.

Wakefield, John Allen (OV-A5)--History of the war between
the United States and the Sac and Fox Nations of Indians,
... in the years 1827, 1831, and 1832. Jacksonville,
Ill., Printed by C. Goudy, 1834. 142p. 3.55 LoC 1846

Walcot, James (TOS-2)--The new Pilgrim's progress; or,
The pious Indian convert. ... London, printed for M.
Cooper, etc. etc., 1748. 5.95 LoC   1847

Waldo, Samuel Putnam (TOS-2)--Memoirs of Andrew
Jackson, ... Hartford, pub. by Silas Andrus, 1818.
5.95 LoC   1848

Walker, Hugh (BC-3)--Three centuries of Scottish literature.
Glasgow, J. Maclehose, 1893. 2v. v1, 8.48; v2,
6.40 LoC   1849

Walker, Leroy T. (PE-400)--A program of professional
preparation for teachers of physical education with
special reference to the needs of youth. 1957. Thesis
(Ph.D.), New York Univ. 312p. 2.45 O   1850

Walker, Margaret C. (RC-47)--A guide for counselor-
in-training programs in girls' private camps. 1958.
Thesis (M.A.), State Univ. of Iowa. 110p. 1.40 O 1851

Walker, Richard Arnold (PE-425)--Changes in body fat
as computed from the skinfold measurement of college
track and field athletes during a season of competition
and training. 1959. Thesis (M.S.), South Dakota
State College. 56p. 1.15 O   1852

219

Walker, Thomas (TOS-2)--Journal of an exploration in the spring of the year 1750. ...With a preface by W.C. Rives. ... Boston, Little, Brown & Co., 1888. 5.95 LoC   1853

Walker, Timothy (OV-A5)--Annual discourse, delivered before the Ohio Historical and Philosophical Society at Columbus, on the 23rd of Dec., 1837. Cincinnati, A. Flash, 1838. 27p. 2.50   LoC   1854

Wallis, Earl L. (PE-401)--Factors related to the recruitment of young men for physical education teaching. 1957. Thesis (Ed.D.), Univ. of Southern California. 387p. 2.85 O   1855

Walts--William Dean Howells and the house of Harper. 3.15   KU   1856

War ships for the southern Confederacy (AP-1): report of public meeting in the Free-trade Hall, Manchester, with letter from Prof. Goldwin Smith to the "Daily News." Manchester, Union & Emancipation Soc., 1863. 34p. 2.45   LoC   1857

Ward, James Warner (OV-A5)--The song of higher water. New York, R.H. Johnston & Co. ...1868. 30p. 2.50   LoC   1858

Warden, David Baillie (TOS-2)--A statistical, political, and historical account of the United States of North America;... Edinburgh, printed for A. Constable & Co. ... 1819. 3v. 5.95 each   LoC   1859

Warton, Thomas (BC-3)--History of English poetry from the 12th to the close of the 16th century ... with a preface by Richard Price, and notes variorum. Ed. by W. Carew Hazlitt. With new notes and other additions. London, Reeves & Turner, 1741. 4v. v1, 6.81; v2, 3, 4, 4.82 each   LoC   1860

Washington, George (TOS-2)--Diaries ... 1748-1799, ed. by J.C. Fitzpatrick ... Pub. for the Mount Vernon Ladies Assoc. of the Union. Boston & New York, Houghton, Mifflin Co., 1925. 4v. 5.95 each LoC   1861

--------(TOS-3)--Journal ... Williamsburg, printed by
  Wm. Hunter, 1854. 5.95 LoC   1862

--------(TOS-4)--Journal of my journey over the mountains;
  ... while surveying for Lord Thomas Fairfax, ...
  Copied from the original with literal exactness and ed.
  with notes by J.M. Toner. Albany, N.Y., Munsell's
  Sons, 1892. 5.95 LoC   1863

Waterhouse, Edward (TOS-4)--A declaration of the state
  of the colony and affaires in Virginia. ... Published
  by authoritie. London, imprinted by G. Eld. for
  R. Mylbourne, 1622. 5.95 LoC   1864

Watterson, Henry, 1840 (KC-14)--George Dennison
  (sic) Prentice. A memorial address delivered before
  the legislature of Kentucky in the hall of the House of
  Representatives ... Feb. 2nd, 1870. 5,27p. 3.95
  LoC   1865

Webber, Charles Wilkins (P&R-1, also SB-1)--The gold
  mines of the Gila. A sequel to Old Hicks the guide.
  5.95 LoC   1866

--------(P&R-1, also SB-1)--Old Hicks the guide; or,
  adventures in the Camanche country in search of a gold
  mine. 5.95 LoC   1867

Webster (LR-E&W)--Patent. 2v. (1602-1855). MMP 1868

Weckwerth, Charles Frederick (RC-33)--A guide to the
  planning of curriculum for the pre-professional preparation of recreation leadership. 1957. Thesis (Ed.D.),
  New York Univ. 759p. 4.00 O   1869

Weeden, Miss Howard (S-B3)--Bandanna ballads,
  including "Shadows on the Wall;" verses and pictures.
  Introd. by Joel Chandler Harris. New York, Doubleday
  & McClure Co., 1899. 90p. 3.25 LoC   1870

Weeden, W.B.--Economic and social history of New
  England, 1620-1789. 2v. 7.50 SM   1871

Welsh, C.--A bookseller of the last century, being some
  account of the life of John Newberry. 3.50 SM   1872

Welsh, Mary Ann (ACRL-112)--Andrew Marschalk,
Mississippi's first printer. 1957. Thesis (M.L.S.),
Univ. of Mississippi. .75 UR   1873

Wentworth, William Fitzwilliam Milton & Walter Butler
Cheadle (P&R-1)--The north-west passage by land.
Being the narrative of an expedition from Atlantic to
the Pacific, undertaken with the view of exploring a
route across the continent to British Columbia through
British territory, ... 5.95 LoC   1874

Wesley, Charles (TOS-4)--The Journal of the Rev. Charles
Wesley, ... To which are appended, Selections from his
correspondence and poetry. With an introd. and
occasional notes, by T. Jackson. London, 1849.
2v. 5.95 each   LoC   1875

Wesley, John (TOS-1)--An extract of the Rev. Mr. John
Wesley's journal from his embarking for Georgia to his
return to London. Reprinted from mss.: The journal
of the Rev. John Wesley, A.M., ed. by N. Curnock.
Bristol, Eng., S. & F. Farley [1739] 5.95 LoC   1876

West, Charlotte (PE-383)--A comparative study between
height and wall volley tests scores as related to volleyball
playing ability of girls and women. 1957. Thesis
(M.Ed.), Woman's College, Univ. of North Carolina.
57p. 1.05 O   1877

West, John (P&R-1)--The substance of a journal during
a residence at the Red River Colony, British North
America; and frequent excursions among the North-
West American Indians, in the years 1820-23. 5.95
LoC   1878

The Western Souvenir (MFM, also OV-A1). 1829. 6.29
LoC   1879

Western's Tithe Cases (LR-E&W)--Tithe. 1v. (1535-
1822). MMP   1880

Wetmore, Alphonso (P&R-2)--Gazetteer of the State of
Missouri. ... Containing frontier sketches and
illustrations of Indian character. ... 5.95 LoC 1881

Wienpahl, Robert W.--The emergence of tonality. 1953.
Thesis (Ph.D.), Univ. of California (Los Angeles).
3.75   UR   1882

Wheeler, Joseph--Children of Joseph and Daniella Wheeler.
By Jos. & Daniella Wheeler. Wheeler, Ala. [n.d.] 24p.
.80   GML   1883

Whipple, Charles King (AP-1)--The family relation, as
affected by slavery. Cincinnati, O., American Reform
Tract & Book Soc., 1858. 24p. 2.45 LoC   1884

Whitaker, Alexander (TOS-1)--Good newes from Virginia. ...
At London, imprinted by F. Kyngston for Wm. Welby,...
1613. 5.95 LoC   1885

White, Andrew (TOS-1)--A Relation of Maryland; together
with a map of the country, ... trans. into English.
London, Wm. Peasley, 1635. 5.95 LoC   1886

White, Richard Grant, 1821 (AP-1)--The new gospel of peace,
according to St. Benjamin. Book second. New York,
Sinclair Tousey, 1863. 48p. 2.45 LoC   1887

White, W.P.--The modern calorimeter. 1928. ACS monograph no. 42. 5.80 MXT   1888

Whitefield, George (TOS-4)--The works of the Rev. George
Whitefield, ... containing all his sermons and tracts, ...
London, printed for E. & C. Dilly, 1771-72. 6v. 5.95
each LoC   1889

Whiting, Henry (OV-A5)--Ontwa, the son of the forest. A
poem. New-York, Wiley & Halsted, 1822. 136p. 3.49
LoC   1890

--------(OV-A5)--Sanillac, a poem. With notes by Lewis
Cass and Henry R. Schoolcraft, esqs. Boston, Carter &
Babcock, 1831. 155p. 3.70   LoC   1891

Wilberg, Robert B. (PSY-103)--Hand-eye coordination
determined by the variability in visual and motor errors.
1960. Thesis (M.S.), Univ. of Oregon. 116p. 1.40
O   1892

Wild, Ebenezer (TOS-4)--Journal ...(1776-1781)....Cam-
bridge, Mass. [Mass. Hist. Soc.] 1891 5.95 LoC 1893

Wilders, R.I.--Extracts from the Book of the Wilders...
to Nicholas Wilder of England, 1845. Sketch of
Wilkinson family. By Mary R. (Wilder) Turner.
With typed index. Springfield, Ohio, 1927. 19p.
.95   GML   1894

Wildlife Disease Association. Journal. No. 1-3, 1959,
completed; no. 4-5, 1959 in prep. membership basis
AI   1895

Wilhelm, Paul, Duke of Württemberg (TOS-4)--Erste
Reise nach dem nördlichen Amerika in den Jahren
1822 bis 1824. Stuttgart & Tubingen, J.G. Cotta,
1835. 5.95 LoC   1896

Willett, Edward, 1830 (KC-12)--Old Honesty; or, The
guests of the Beehalt Tavern. A tale of the early days
of Kentucky. New York, Beadle & Adams (1867).
100p. 2.59 LoC   1897

--------(KC-12)--The Shawnee scout; or, The death
trail. By J. Stanley Henderson (pseud.). New York,
Beadle & Adams (1870). (Beadle's pocket series, no.211)
98p. 2.50   LoC   1898

Williams--Marlowe; the buried name--a romantic melo-
drama. .70   KU   1899

--------Parrhasius: a Southern returns to the classics.
.35   KU   1900

--------Selected works of Espy Williams: Southern
playwright. 2.80 KU   1901

Williams, M.W.--Anglo-American Isthmian diplomacy,
1815-1915. 2.50 SM   1902

Williams, William (TOS-4)--Journal of the life, travels
and gospel labours, ... Cincinnati, Lodge, L'Hommedieu
& Hammond, 1828. 5.95 LoC   1903

Willmore, Wollaston & Daveson (LR-E&W)--King's Bench.
1v. (1837). MMP   1904

Willmore, Wollaston & Hodges (LR-E&W)--King's Bench.
2v. (1838-39). MMP   1905

Wilmer, Richard Hooker, bp. (S-B4)--The recent past
from a Southern standpoint. Reminiscences of a
grandfather. New York, T. Whittaker, 1887. 281p.
3.95   LoC   1906

Wilmot, Franklin A. (KC-8)--Disclosures and confessions
of Frank A. Wilmot, the slave thief and Negro runner.
With an account of the Underground Railroad. Philadelphia,
Barclay & Co., 1860. 38p. 2.50   LoC   1907

Wilson, Alexander (TOS-3)--American ornithology; or,
The natural history of the birds of the United States;
... Philadelphia, Bradford & Inskeep, 1808-14. 9v.
5.95 each   LoC   1908

Wilson, Samuel (TOS-1)--An account of the Province of
Carolina in America. ... London, printed by G.
Larkin for F. Smith, 1682. 5.95   LoC   1909

Wilson, Thomas (TOS-1)--A brief journal of the life,
travels and labours of love in the work of the ministry,
... Dublin, printed by and for S. Fuller, 1728. 5.95
LoC   1910

Wilstach, John Augustine (OV-A5)--The battle forest;
a poem. (New York, Press of American Bank Note
Co.) c.1890. 18p. 2.50   LoC   1911

Wing, Mary Jane (ACRL-119)--A history of the School of
Library Science of the University of North Carolina;
the first twenty-five years. 1958. Thesis (M.S. in
L.S.), Univ. of North Carolina. 1.50   UR   1912

Winn, Jerome Edward (PE-402)--Soccer knowledge test
for college men. 1957. Thesis (P.E.D.), Indiana Univ.
106p. 1.65   O   1913

Winthrop, Theodore (P&R-1)--John Brent. 5.95   LoC   1914

Wislizenus, Adolphus (OV-A5, also P&R-1)--Einausflug
nach den Felsen-gebirgen in Jahre 1839. St. Louis,
Mo., W. Weber, 1840. 122p. 3.33   LoC   1915

--------(P&R-1)--Memoir of a tour to northern Mexico,
connected with Col. Doniphan's expedition, in 1846-47.
5.95   LoC   1916

Witherspoon, Pattie French (KC-11)--Through two
   administrations, character sketches of Kentucky.
   Chicago, T.B. Arnold, 1897. 110p. 2.70 LoC   1917

Wolfbein, S.L.--The decline of a textile city; a study of
   New Bedford. 2.00 SM   1918

Wolferstan & Bristowe (LR-E&W)--Election. 1v.
   (1859-65). MMP   1919

Wolferstan & Dew (LR-E&W)--Election. 1v. (1856-
   58). MMP   1920

Wollaston (LR-E&W)--Bail. 1v. (1840-41). MMP   1921

Wood, Anthony A. (BC-3)--Athenae oxonienses...
   a new ed. with additions, and a continuation by Philip
   Bliss. London, Printed for F.C. & J. Rivington,
   1813-20. 5v. v1, 5.40; v2, 3, 4, 5   3.41 each LoC1922

Woods, John (OV-A5)--Shakerism unmasked; or, A
   narrative showing the entrance of the Shakers into the
   western country, ... Paris, Ky., Printed at the
   office of the Western Observer, 1826. 84p. 2.91
   LoC   1923

--------(TOS-3)--Two years' residence in the settlement
   on the English prairie, in the Illinois country, ...
   London, Longman, ... 1822. 5.95 LoC   1924

Woods, Marcella Darlene (PH-63)--The effectiveness of
   an endurance swimming program on the physical
   fitness of college women as related to cardio-vascular
   condition, physique, and motor fitness. 1958.
   Thesis (M.Ed.), Woman's College, Univ. of North
   Carolina. 100p. 1.40 O   1925

Wood's Tithe Cases (LR-E&W)--Tithe. 4v. (1650-1798).
   MMP   1926

Woolman, John (TOS-4)--A journal of the life, gospel
   labours, and Christian experiences ... In The Works
   of John Woolman. In two parts. Philadelphia,
   printed by Joseph Crukshank, 1774. Pt. 1. 5.95
   LoC   1927

Worthington, Thomas, 1807 (AP-1)--A correct history of
the Battle of Shiloh, ... Washington, T. McGill & Co.,
printers, 1880. 20p. 2.45 LoC   1928

Wright, John W. (P&R-1)--Chivington's massacre of the
Cheyenne Indians. 5.95 LoC   1929

Wright, T.G.--Literary culture in early New England,
1620-1730. 2.00 SM   1930

Wyeth, John B. (P&R-2)--Oregon; or a short history of
a long journey from the Atlantic Ocean to the region of
the Pacific, by land; drawn up from the notes and oral
information of ... the only one who has returned to
New England. 5.95 LoC   1931

Wylie, Andrew (OV-A5)--An address delivered before the
Philomathean Society of Wabash College. July 10, 1838.
Bloomington, Ia., Printed at the Franklin Office
(1838). 24p. 2.50 LoC   1932

Y

Yanagita, Kunio--Japanese folklore dictionary. 5.95
KU   1933

Yoakum, Henderson K. (S-B4)--History of Texas from
its first settlement in 1685 to its annexation by the
United States in 1846 ... with an extended appendix.
New York, Redfield, 1856. 2v. illus. 3.95 each
LoC   1934

Yonge, Francis (TOS-1)--A Narrative of the Proceedings
of the people of South-Carolina, in the year 1719; ...
London, printed in the year 1726. 5.95 LoC   1935

--------(TOS-1)--A view of the trade of South-Carolina,
... [London, 1722?]   5.95 LoC   1936

Young, Arthur (TOS-4)--Observations on the present
state of the waste lands of Great Britain. ...London,
printed for W. Nicoll, 1773. 5.95 LoC   1937

Young, Jacob (TOS-2)--Autobiography of a Pioneer; ...
Cincinnati, Cranston & Curts, 1857. 5.95 LoC   1938

Young, Lot D., 1842 (AP-1)--Reminiscences of a soldier
of the Orphan Brigade. Louisville, Courier-Journal
Prtg. Co., 1897. 99p. 2.45 LoC   1939

Young, Vera Price (PSY-121)--Reminiscence and its effect
on learning selected badminton skills. 1958. Thesis
(M.A.), State Univ. of Iowa. 59p. 1.15 O   1940

Young, W.A. (TOS-3)--The history of North and South
America, ... To which is added an impartial enquiry
into the present American disputes. London, printed
for J. Whitaker, 1776. 2v. 5.95 each   LoC   1941

Z

Zedler, Dr. G. --Die alteste Gutenbergtype. -Veröff.
der Gutenberg-Gesellschaft 1. Mainz, 1902. Nr.6-8.
MK   1942

Zeppelin, Ferdinand Graf von--Denkschrift über den Bau
eines lenkbaren Luftschiffes, Als Manuskript gedruckt.
Stuttgart, 1895. Nr.200. MK   1943

Zeitschrift fuer Anorganische Chemie. Vols. 1-252
(1892-1944). 625.00 MXT   1944

Zeitschrift fuer Kristallographie, Mineralogie, und
Petrographie. Vols. 1-106 (1877-1945). 609.50
C   1945

Zoological Record. Pisces Section. Vols. 1-85.
25.00 F   1946

Camping--See Recreation and camping.

Cattle trade, 1380.

Chemistry, 192, 264, 436-37, 1029, 1164, 1459, 1567, 1755, 1815, 1888, 1944.

Child study, 442.

Civil service, 720.

Coaldwell family, 386.

Coldwell family, 386.

Corning, H., ed., 105.

Corporation reports, 69.

Craig, Dr. James S., 182.

Defense research, 78.

Drama, 619, 778, 1754, 1774.

Drummond, Josiah H., 1560.

Early music books--See Music, Early Books.

Economics, 8, 304, 560, 644, 903, 1036, 1039, 1355, 1575, 1796, 1871.

Eddy, Ruth S.D., 886.

Edes, Richard S., 1242.

Education, 961, 1037.

Education, Psychology of, 310.

Entomology, 1035.

Exercise, Physiology of--See Physiology of exercise.

Family histories--See Genealogy.

Genealogy, 26-28, 107, 145, 174, 361, 386-88, 495, 594, 886, 922, 953, 958, 975, 1097, 1111, 1525, 1547, 1560, 1589, 1597, 1624, 1633, 1700, 1883, 1894.

General science--See Science, General.

Genet, Edmond Charles, 1258.

Geography, 1040.

Geology, 1945.

Hall, John, ed., 22.

Health education, 11, 175, 273, 784, 789, 795, 865, 889, 1105, 1154, 1262, 1366, 1381, 1429, 1433, 1546, 1554, 1628, 1679.

Heiskell family, 975.

Hinton, Richard, 1510.

History--See also lists under main entries: British Culture Microcards, Kentucky Culture Series, Nineteenth Century American Literature, Nineteenth Century American Pamphlets, The Plains and the Rockies, Travels in the Old South, 13, 65, 113, 287, 389, 484, 487-88, 656, 877, 915, 1064, 1135, 1145, 1367, 1411, 1440, 1454, 1468, 1616, 1625, 1688, 1710, 1751, 1811-12, 1818-20, 1871.

Horticulture, 50

Icthyology, 42, 247, 530, 1817, 1946.

Language, 1297, 1358, 1499, 1933.

Law--See also Pre-1865 Law Reports [England and Wales], 441, 938, 972, 1053, 1344, 1823, 1827-28.

Lea, James H., 174.

Leidy, Joseph, 882.

Library science--See also ACRL Microcard Series--
764-66, 810, 966, 1235, 1603, 1749.

Literature--See also lists under main entries: British
Culture on Microcards, Kentucky Culture Series,
Nineteenth Century American Literature, Mike Fink
Miscellany--731, 878, 1052, 1541, 1636, 1797.

Literature, Criticism, 7, 179-80, 492, 588, 596, 685,
760, 770, 857, 890, 990, 1099, 1114, 1158, 1171,
1378, 1467, 1474, 1476, 1699, 1709, 1729, 1736,
1746, 1839, 1856, 1899-1901, 1930,

Lighter than air craft--See Balloons,

Magic lanterns, 655, 1519.

Medicine, 47, 250, 311, 395-97, 513, 837, 1041, 1238,
1247, 1339, 1427, 1588.

Metals, production, 1814.

Microbiology, 70.

Microphotography, 1107.

Music, Early Books, 18, 30, 66, 92, 137, 215, 222-23,
266, 375, 406, 444, 502-04, 523, 592, 682, 830, 899,
1054, 1059, 1088, 1102-04, 1112, 1117, 1120, 1123,
1131-32, 1140, 1170, 1202-04, 1212-13, 1221-30,
1237, 1257, 1294, 1313, 1347, 1403-04, 1469, 1498,
1515, 1677, 1695, 1744, 1803.

Music, General, 21, 769, 835, 1333, 1882.

Mycology, 218.

Natural history, 1895.

New York stock exchange reports, 69.

Nuclear science, 1363.

Oceanography, 1629.

Osborne, John, 107.

Page, Thomas Nelson, 802.

Paleontology, 1042.

Parasitology, 1043.

Parshall, James C., 145.

Patents, 1815, 1824.

Periodicals, General, 490, 1342, 1690.

Petroleum geology, 39.

Petrology, 1046, 1945.

Philosophy, 400, 1045, 1304.

Physics, 1258, 1434.

Physical education, 36, 49, 76, 181, 254, 291, 330, 335-36,
    365, 458, 553, 566-67, 657, 676, 681, 690, 750, 820,
    861, 864, 868, 873, 896, 898, 908, 925, 937, 957, 965,
    1005, 1091, 1094, 1100, 1142, 1149, 1159, 1166, 1217,
    1246, 1299, 1308, 1334-35, 1398, 1428, 1448, 1456,
    1502-03, 1521, 1561-62, 1565, 1578, 1596, 1614, 1640,
    1653, 1661, 1705, 1727, 1739, 1771, 1850, 1852, 1855,
    1877, 1913.

Physiology of exercise, 172, 191, 352, 367, 497, 512, 591,
    768, 825, 1063, 1178, 1241, 1559, 1600, 1660, 1832,
    1835, 1925.

Political science, 51, 389, 403, 475, 486-88, 645, 648, 741,
    903, 1206, 1355, 1406, 1411, 1811-12, 1816, 1825, 1902.

Printing, history of, 89, 467, 731, 904, 1500, 1763, 1872, 1942.

Prisons, 1160.

Psychiatry, 44.

Psychology, 6, 219, 269, 456, 463-64, 479, 528, 578, 586, 740, 780, 794, 821, 851, 872, 883, 891, 897, 914, 989, 999, 1030, 1032, 1034, 1044, 1095, 1167, 1196, 1329-30, 1332, 1348, 1365, 1374, 1471-73, 1519, 1526, 1529, 1604, 1613, 1639, 1686, 1689, 1726, 1731, 1802, 1843-44, 1892, 1940.

Psychology of education--See Education, Psychology of.

Recreation and camping, 283, 430, 541, 788, 815, 949, 969, 991, 1056, 1106, 1129, 1195, 1356, 1533, 1581, 1584, 1592, 1630, 1851, 1869.

Religion, 401, 625, 715, 730, 1098, 1211, 1273-74, 1304, 1402, 1430, 1582.

Saunders, H.S., 489.

Schönwetter, Theobald, ed., 1376.

Science, General, 45, 992, 1617.

Science, History of, 191, 264, 917, 1567, and list under main entry: History of Science

Smith, S.H., ed., 617.

Sociology, 46, 404, 489, 1030, 1580, 1918.

Stock and stock breeding, 1031.

Stock exchange reports, 69.

Theology--See Religion.

Traubel, Horace, ed., 489.

Veterinary medicine, 48.

Walbaum, Johann Julius, ed., 90.

Williams, Roger, 1328.

Zoology, 1435, 1946.